Filled with music, garlanded with fresh colors — from joyous cover to cover this book says: I love you. Its 324 pages contain the tenderest love songs and the most impassioned the world has known.

## Love Songs in Every Mood

Here are the romantic melodies and poignant lyrics that lovers have loved over the centuries. They range from *Kathleen Mavourneen* and the haunting *Black Is the Color of My True Love's Hair* to Verdi's *Celeste Aïda,* from the sentimental *Love's Old Sweet Song* to what is possibly the most magnificent of all tributes to a beloved, Handel's great aria, *Where'er You Walk.*

While most of the songs are American, English, and Irish, the book includes songs from many other countries that have found their way to American hearts. And there are songs by composers who belong to all the world, among them Schumann, Brahms, Haydn, Scarlatti, Pergolesi, Mozart, Schubert, and Purcell.

## How This Book Was Made

*The Fireside Book of Love Songs* was prepared under the brilliant direction of Margaret Bradford Boni, with musical arrangements by Norman Lloyd of the Juilliard School. The paintings (reproduced in all their subtle coloring) are by Alice and Martin Provensen, the superbly talented young couple who work together as one artist—so that no one (not even the publishers) knows what each contributes.

These are the same four people who made the famous *Fireside Book of Folk Songs,* which has thus far found its way into more than 200,000 American homes. In *The Fireside Book of Love Songs* they have surpassed themselves.

And this time another—and very distinguished—voice has been added. There is an interpretive introduction by the gentle and witty philosopher, Irwin Edman.

# FIRESIDE BOOK OF

# Love Songs

SELECTED AND EDITED BY MARGARET BRADFORD <u>BONI</u>, *ed.*

ARRANGED FOR THE PIANO BY NORMAN LLOYD

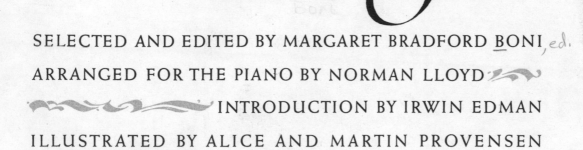

INTRODUCTION BY IRWIN EDMAN

ILLUSTRATED BY ALICE AND MARTIN PROVENSEN

*SIMON AND SCHUSTER ► NEW YORK*

⊏1954⊐

To Ruth and Charlie

# CONTENTS

## SONGS FROM THE GREAT COMPOSERS

# INTRODUCTION

*by Irwin Edman*

THE SONGS gathered in this volume point up the arresting fact that for the generality of mankind—and these songs come from many civilized countries of the globe—love is not something necessarily reserved, arcane and mystical, nor something merely to be dissected intellectually. It is something sweet and something sad. It has its gaieties and its ironies; it has its smiles and its tears. It happens not to genius only; it is droll more often than it is sublime. It is something as simple as sunlight and Spring, as dusk or Autumn. The familiar love songs of mankind are a breviary of an emotion simple enough to be known to all, or nearly all, mankind.

The most widely beloved of love songs are not, as the mere table of contents of this book will show, celebrations of ecstasy; they are not rhapsodic hymns of adoration. They are quiet, by and large, and familiar. They are the minstrelsy of old and cherished affections, they celebrate—or recall—the dear well-known or well-remembered ways of the beloved, the companionship mellowed by years, the grief whose sharper pangs have been subdued by memory. If the beloved is praised, it is not with the eloquent excesses of the Song of Solomon; it is rather with the whisper of affection too shy to speak in superlatives. Nor can one help noticing that the most widely enduring songs are not, except by indirection, erotic. Affection, memory, regret tinctured with tenderness, the pathos of distance and of separation, or the simplicities of companionship—it is both odd and striking that the love songs that have survived for generations are marked by such relatively muted emotions as these.

The songs in this collection are specifically so familiar that they demand almost no exposition and no commentary. They range from bumpkin humor to feelings sometimes cozy, sometimes rapturous. "My luve is like a red, red rose that's newly sprung in June" is not Sappho, but it *is* Robert Burns, and Burns speaking as all good poets do, at once in his own voice and in that of all his compatriots and all his fellow mortals when they happen to be lovers. The music ranges, too, from folk tunes to the most knowing craftsmanship, the most unmistakable genius. Brahms, Haydn, Schumann, Schubert and that prolific and inventive melodist, Alessandro Scarlatti. The cadence of the folk song, the rhythm of the subtlest of artist-musicians, have found their way into what might be described as an anthology of sounds.

These melodies are simple, though often very artfully so. They sing themselves through the modest melodic means direct to the heart. Sometimes the musical materials are melodies that originate anonymously in such a town as contained "Sally in Our Alley" or where there was, as in the old American song, "a tavern in the town," or among people who would feel the allusions of "Comin' thro' the Rye," or "When the Corn Is Waving, Annie Dear." Sometimes the sentiments, still simple and heartfelt, are conveyed in melodies like those of Mozart whose ease and directness are deceptive. To the musically trained listener, "Voi che sapete" ("You Who Are Knowing") is more than a touching aria in which the adolescent heart tells its elders how it is at once troubled and enchanted by love. The song is something more; it is a matchless little work of knowing musical art, as is "Ich liebe dich" of Beethoven.

Schubert is perhaps the perfect instance of the point at which art and feeling meet and of the common quality at which the most naïve and sentimental of enduringly popular love songs blend with the most civilized musical art. "L'il Liza Jane," an American folk song, is not Schubert's "Du bist die Ruh," either musically or in spirit. But both survive not for musical reasons only, not even Schubert's exquisite masterpiece. They endure because they catch a note intimate and universal (though each a different one) of the same basic feeling. But in the hands of a great artist a commonplace turns into something rare to the point almost of strangeness. Many lovers have found in the name and being of their beloved the name and being of peace, of ultimate serenity, of silent happiness. Schubert's song says all this with heartbreaking aptness; the voice utters it following the melodic line almost more than the words and the piano accompaniment is a perfect wordless commentary.

It is not for nothing that the German romantic composers have been thought by many to be the most perfect articulators in music. For them the music was not the food of love but its very language. But there are more homely, less expert voicings of the variations of love, of companionship and even of humor. The German romantic composers found a technique for letting the heart speak at once subtly and with disarming human sweetness. But the art of music has spoken through talent as well as genius, and through nameless creators of artless felicities of feeling and of form. The Irish "Down by the Salley Gardens" sings itself disarmingly into eternal fame. "The Last Rose of Summer" is sung, over and over again, often very poorly indeed, by some homespun singer, some homely group. It does not matter that these songs vary in artistic quality. There are many that have had, for reasons not always entitled to be called genius, at least the genius of survival. And that implies, after all, a gift. Where artless words, where naïve music is sung generation after generation, it bespeaks something intimate, warm and even deep.

The familiar songs are touching not only because they are about love, and seem to catch its very cadence, but because they are about the warm familiar things, youth remembered, and partings and sorrows, and some special tenderness that the words and the melodies conjure up to each listener—someone loved wisely, or too little, or in vain, someone who means or meant peace, who means or meant beauty, who is like a flower, who is like a red, red rose, who is or was happiness. No wonder these songs survive.

# SONGS FROM MANY COUNTRIES

# Love's Old Sweet Song

A. Clifton Bingham

J. L. Molloy

*Gently*

1. Once in the dear, dead days be-yond re-call, When on the world the
2. E - ven to-day we hear Love's song of yore, Deep in our hearts it

mists be-gan to fall, Out of the dreams that rose in hap-py throng,
dwells for - ev - er more, Foot-steps may fal - ter, wea-ry grow the way,

Low in our hearts Love sang an old sweet song; And in the dusk where
Still we can hear it at the close of day; So till the end when

fell the fire - light gleam, Soft - ly it wove it - self in -
life's dim shad- ows fall, Love will be found the sweet - est

to our dream.
song of all.

Just a song at twi - light,

Chorus Slowly but with movement

Slowly but with movement

when the lights are low, And the flick - 'ring shad - ows

# The Dove Has Twin White Feet

Serbian song

*Very freely*

1. The dove has twin white feet so fair, And two white wings a-
2. He brings them to his cas- tle twain, And ask -eth of each

loft that may bear, And two sweet maids my lord lead -eth there.
fair one so fain Which choos-eth she as her do- main.

3. And she that was the fairest there
Laughed lightly as did she thus declare
The lovelier shall mine be as share.

4. But she that loved the most did say,
"There only, dear one, dwell I may
Where my true love shall ever stay."

23

# Black Is the Color
# of My True Love's Hair

American song

Slowly, with intensity

*mp* d min.    g min.    F maj.7   a min.7   d min.    a min.7

—1. Black, black, black is the col-or of my true love's hair; Her lips are
2. Oh, I love my — love — and — well she knows; I love the

-won - drous ros - y fair, The pret - tiest face and the dain - tiest
ground where-on __ she goes. If you no more on __ earth __ I

hands, I love the ground where - on she stands.
see I can't serve you as you have me.

*deliberately*

3. Winter's passed and the leaves now again are green;
   The time has passed that we have seen.
   But still I hope the time will come
   When you and I shall be as one.

4. I now go to Clyde to mourn and weep;
   But satisfied I never could sleep.
   I'll write to you in a few short lines,
   I'll suffer death ten thousand times.

5. Black, black, black is the color of my true love's hair;
   Her lips are wondrous rosy fair,
   The prettiest face and the daintiest hands,
   I love the ground whereon she stands.

# Love Somebody, Yes I Do

American song

Love some-bod-y, **yes I** do; Love some-bod-y, yes I do;

Love some-bod-y, yes I do; Love some-bod-y, but I won't tell who.

Love some-bod-y, yes I do; Love some-bod-y, yes I do;

Love some-bod-y, yes I do;
1. And I hope some-bod-y loves me too.
2. 'Tween__ six - teen and twen-ty-two.

# AURA LEE

W. W. Fosdick                                           George R. Poulton

*Simply*

1. As the black-bird in the spring, — 'Neath the wil-low tree, —
2. On her cheek the rose was born,'Twas mu-sic when she spake; —

Sat and piped, I heard him sing, — Sing of Au-ra Lee.
In her eyes the rays of morn With sud-den splen-dor break.

**Chorus**

Au - ra Lee! Au - ra Lee! Maid of gold - en hair,

Sun -shine came a - long with thee, And swal-lows in the air.

# Sally in Our Alley

Henry Carey

1. Of all the
2. Of all the

girls __ that are so smart, __ There's none like pret-ty Sal-ly; She is the
days __ with-in the week __ I dear - ly love but one day, And that's the

Verse 1: dar - ling of my heart, \_\_ And lives in our \_\_ al - ley; There's
Verse 2: day \_ that comes be - twixt \_ A Sat - ur- day and Mon-day: O,

Verse 1: ne'er a la - dy in the land Is half so sweet as Sal-ly; She is the
Verse 2: then I'm dressed all in my best To walk a-broad with Sal-ly; She is the

Verse 1: dar - ling of my heart, \_\_ And \_ lives in our \_\_ al - ley.
Verse 2: dar - ling of my heart, \_\_ And \_ lives in our \_\_ al - ley.

3. When Christmas comes about again,
   O, then I shall have money;
   I'll save it up, and box and all
   I'll give unto my honey;
   And when my sev'n long years are out,
   O, then I'll marry Sally,
   And then how happily we'll live!
   But not in our alley.

# There Is a Tavern in the Town

American song

*With gusto*

1. There is a tav-ern in the town, in the town, And
2. He left me for a dam-sel dark, dam-sel dark, Each

there my true love sits him down, sits him down,__ And__
Fri- day night they used to spark, used to spark,__ And__

drinks his wine 'mid laugh- ter __ free, And
now my love, once true __ to __ me, Takes

can no long-er stay with you, stay with you, __ I'll __ hang my harp on a weep-ing wil-low tree, And may the world go well with thee.

# Shepherd and Shepherdess

### (ROEH VEROAH)

Translation by Irene Roehr

Versification by Freda Morrill Abrams

Words and music by Matatyahu Shelem

Ey-sham har-heyk beyn he-ha-rim ro-eh ve-ro-ah le-beyn a-da-rim. Hee-loh, hoo-lah,

Up in the moun-tains with their sheep A shep-herd and shep-herd-ess watch do keep. She is his, he is hers,

*shtey ey - na - yim a - ha - vah,* *hee - lo,* ___
Two eyes flam - ing, bright with love. She is his, ___

*hoo - lah,* ___ *shtey ey - na - yim___ le - ha vah.*
he is hers, ___ Two eyes flam - ing,___ light of love.

2. Under the woodland trees they walk,
   The shepherd and shepherdess laugh and talk.
   *Chorus:*

3. Nearby the well his flute notes ring,
   And while he is playing, sweetly she sings.
   *Chorus:*

4. Then comes the ev'ning, dying day,
   And down to the valley they go their way.
   *Chorus:*

5. Gone now the moonlight, dawns the sun,
   And still is the flute now love's dream is done.
   *Chorus:*

CHORUS
She is his, he is hers,
Two eyes flaming, bright with love,
She is his, he is hers,
Two eyes flaming, light of love.

# Long, Long Ago

Words and music by Thomas H. Bayly

*With flowing motion*

1. Tell me the tales that to me were so dear, Long, long a-go,
2. Do you re-mem-ber the path where we met, Long, long a-go,

long, long a-go, Sing me the songs I de-light-ed to hear,
long, long a-go, Ah, yes, you told me you ne'er would for-get,

Long, long, a-go, long a-go. Now you are come all my
Long, long a-go, long a-go. Then to all oth-ers my

grief is re - mov'd, Let me for - get that so long you have rov'd,
smiles you pre - ferred, Love, when you spake, gave a charm to each word,

Let me be - lieve that you love as you lov'd,
Still my heart treas - ure the prais - es I heard,

Long, long a - go, long a - go.
Long, long a - go, long a - go.

# LORENA

J. P. Webster                                                                    Rev. H. D. L. Webster

*Andante sentimentale, ma non troppo*

1. The years creep slow-ly by, Lo-re - na, The
2. We loved each oth-er then, Lo-re - na, More

snow     is   on   the   grass   a - gain,     The
than     we   ev - er   dared   to   tell;       And

sun's    low   down   the   sky,   Lo-re - na,   The
what     we   might   have   been,   Lo-re - na,   Had

frost      gleams where the flow'rs have been.      But the
but      our lov - ing pros - per'd well!      But ___

heart      throbs on as warm - ly now,      As
then,      'tis past – the years are gone,      I'll

when      the sum - mer days were high, ___      The
not      call up their shad- 'wy forms; ___      I'll

sun ... can nev-er dip so low ___ As
say ... to them: "Lost years, sleep on! ___ Sleep

down af-fec-tion's cloud-less sky.
on! Nor heed life's pelt-ing storm."

43

# Sweet Alice, Ben Bolt

Dr. Thomas Dunn

Nelson Kneass

1. Oh! don't you re-mem-ber sweet A-lice, Ben Bolt, Sweet A-lice with hair so brown; She wept with de-light when you gave her a smile And trem-bled with fear at your frown. In the

2. Oh! don't you re-mem-ber the wood, Ben Bolt, Near the sun-ny slope of the hill, Where oft we have sung 'neath the wide spread-ing shade, And kept time to the click of the mill. The

# Ay, ay, ay

English version by Marjorie Harper

Spanish lyrics and music by Osmán Pérez Freire

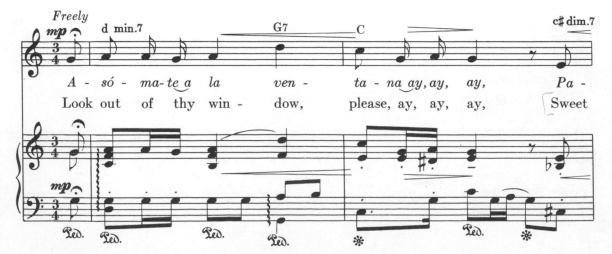

A - só - ma - te_a la ven - ta - na_ay, ay, ay, Pa -
Look out of thy win - dow, please, ay, ay, ay, Sweet

47

ya la au - ro - ra tem - pra - na ay, ay, ay, Nos
out of thy win - dow, dear - est one, ay, ay, ay, A -

vie - ne an - un - ciar el dí - a.
bove us the sun is on its way.

a.
end.

Ay, ay, ay! Ay, ay, ay! _____
Ay, ay, ay! Ay, ay, ay! _____

2. Though thou mayest find thy heart, ay, ay, ay,
 Is empty of love and of romance,
 Then never remind thy heart, ay, ay, ay,
 But welcome each joy that comes perchance.
 Take thou the gifts that the gods send;
 Accept the love that the fates lend.
 Though thou mayest find thy heart alone, ay, ay, ay,
 Yet shelter loves dream unto the end.
 Ay, ay, ay! Ay, ay, ay!

48

# Take Back the Heart
# That Thou Gavest

Words and music by Claribel

With passion

1. Take back the heart that thou gav - est, What is my an-guish to
2. Then when at last o - ver - tak - en, Time flings its fet- ters o'er

# TAKE BACK THE HEART THAT THOU GAVEST

50

# O Fickle Shepherdess

### (BERGÈRE LÉGÈRE)

English version by Lyndal Brandeis

French song

Allegretto—capriciously

*Ber - gè - re lé -*
O shep - herd - ess

*gè - re, Je crains tes ap - pas;___ Ton â - me s'en - flam - me, Mais*
fick - le, Your charms I de - fy;___ Your heart catch-es fire, ___ But

*tu n'ai - mes pas.___ Ta mi - ne mu - ti - ne, Pré - vient___*
love you de - ny.___ Win - some and be - guil - ing, You tempt me

et sé - duit; Mais vai - ne, hau - tai - ne, Tu fuis qui te suit,___ Tu
to pur - sue, But with air dis - dain - ful You fly those who sue,___ You

fuis qui te suit. Ber - gè - re lé - gè - re, Je crains tes ap -
fly those who woo. O shep - herd- ess fick - le, Your charms I de -

pas;___ Ton â - me s'en - flam - me, Mais tu n'ai - mes pas.___
fy; ___ Your heart catch-es fire, ___ But love you de - ny. ___

2. O shepherdess fickle,
   Your charms I defy;
   Your heart catches fire,
   But love you deny.
   Ever singing praises
   Of love and lovers true,
   Empty your pretending,
   You love none but you,
   You love none but you.
   O shepherdess fickle,
   Your charms I defy;
   Your heart catches fire,
   But love you deny.

# The Young Shepherd

## (TO TSOBANOPOULO)

Translation by C. S. Demos
Versification by Freda Morrill Abrams

Greek song

*Tso - ba - na - kos i - moo - na ____ Pro - va - ta - kya fy - la - ga. ____*
I was once a shep - herd lad ____ Keep - ing sheep, was al - ways glad. ____

From *Work and Sing*, an International Songbook, published and copyright 1948 by Cooperative Recreation Service, Delaware, Ohio.

2. Morning, evening, flute I play,
   Making music night and day.
   Why am I in love? Tell me why?
   For vain love I'll surely die!
   *Chorus:* Toonde, toonde, toonde, toonde, toonde, toonde, toonde, toonde.

3. Over all the hills I climb,
   Searching my love all the time,
   Looking for a lithe young shepherdess
   Who has brought my heart distress.
   *Chorus:* Toonde, toonde, toonde, toonde, toonde, toonde, toonde, ah!

57

# Weel May the Keel Row

Scottish song

1. O who is like my John - nie, So leish, so blythe, so
2. He has nae mair o' learn - ing Than tells his week - ly

bon - nie? He's fore - most 'mang the mon - y Keel - lads o' coal - y
earn - ing, Yet right frae wrang dis - cern - ing, Tho' brave, nae bruis - er

Tyne. He'll set or row so tight - ly, Or in the dance so
he. Tho' he's no worth a plack is, His ain' coat on his

spright- ly, He'll cut and shuf-fle sight -ly –'Tis true, were he not mine.
back — is, And nane can say that black is The white o' John - nie's e'e.

*Chorus*

Weel may the keel row, The keel row, the keel — row,

Weel may the keel row That my — lad's — in.

3. He wears a blue bonnet,
   Blue bonnet, blue bonnet,
   He wears a blue bonnet—
   A dimple's in his chin.
   As I cam' thro' Sandgate,
   Thro' Sandgate, thro' Sandgate,
   As I cam' thro' Sandgate
   I heard a lassie sing:

CHORUS

Weel may the keel row,
The keel row, the keel row,
Weel may the keel row
That my lad's in.

59

# Li'l Liza Jane

American song

*Allegro*

1. I knows a gal that you don't know, Li'l Li - za Jane,
2. Li - za ___ Jane looks good to me, Li'l Li - za Jane,

'Way down south in Bal - ti - mo', Li'l Li - za Jane.
Sweet - es' one I ev - er see, Li'l Li - za Jane.

O, E - li - za, Li'l Li - za Jane!

O, E - li - za, Li'l Li - za Jane!

3. Where she lives de posies grow, Li'l Liza Jane,
   Chickens roun' de kitchen do', Li'l Liza Jane.
   *Chorus:*

4. What do I care how far we roam? Li'l Liza Jane,
   Where she's at is home, sweet home, Li'l Liza Jane.
   *Chorus:*

CHORUS
O Eliza, Li'l Liza Jane!
O Eliza, Li'l Liza Jane!

# Caleno Custure Me*

English song

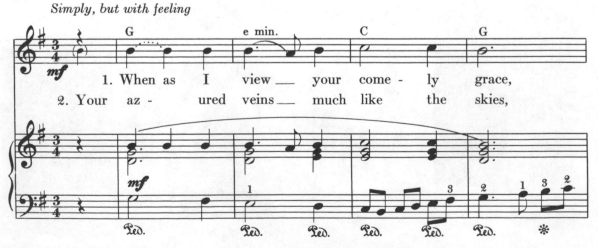

*Simply, but with feeling*

*mf*

1. When as I view ___ your come - ly grace,
2. Your az - ured veins ___ much like the skies,

*A perversion of the Irish* Cailinog a stuir me—*"Young girl, my treasure!"*

62

Cal - en - o ___ Cus - tu - re me. Your
Your

gol - den hair and your an - gel face, ___
cor - al lips, ___ your crys - tal eyes, ___

Cal - en - o ___ Cus - tu - re me.

# Kathleen Aroon

Mrs. Crawford

Franz Abt

1. Why should we part - ed be, Kath - leen A - roon,
2. Give me thy gen - tle hand, Kath - leen A - roon,

When thy fond heart's with me, Kath - leen A - roon!
Come to the hap - py land, Kath - leen A - roon!

Come to these gold-en skies, Bright days for us may rise,
Come o'er the waves with me, These hands shall toil for thee,

Oh! dry those tear-ful eyes, Kath-leen A-roon.
This heart will faith-ful be, Kath-leen A-roon.

*poco rit.*

*a tempo*

3. Why should we parted be, Kathleen Aroon,
When thy fond heart's with me, Kathleen Aroon!
Oh! leave these weeping skies,
Where man a martyr dies,
Come dry those tearful eyes,
Kathleen Aroon.

65

# In the Gloaming

Mete Orred

Annie F. Harrison

*Andante*

1. In the gloam - ing, O my dar - ling! When the lights are
2. In the gloam - ing, O my dar - ling! Think not bit - ter -

dim and low, And the qui - et shad - ows fall - ing,
ly of me! 'Tho I passed a - way in si - lence,

Soft - ly come and soft - ly go. When the winds are
Left you lone - ly, set you free. For my heart was

sob - bing_ faint - ly    With    a    gen - tle,    un - known woe,
crushed with_ long - ing,    What    had been could    nev - er    be.

Will    you think    of    me    and love    me    As    you
It    was best    to    leave    you thus,    dear,    Best for

did    once    long    a - go?
you    and    best    for    me.    It    was best to leave you

thus, _____    Best for    you    and    best    for    me. _____

# Who Will Shoe Your Pretty Little Foot?

American song

68

3. You know a crow is a coal, coal black,
   And turns to a purple blue;
   And if ever I prove false to you,
   I hope my body may melt like dew.

4. I'll love you till the seas run dry,
   And rocks dissolve by the sun;
   I'll love you till the day I die,
   And then you know I'm done.

# Mother, Shall I Now Relate?

## (AH! VOUS DIRAI-JE, MAMAN?)

English version by Freda Morrill Abrams

French song

*Rather plaintively, but not slowly*

Ah! Vous di - rai - je, ma - man, Ce qui cau - se mon tour-ment?
Moth-er, shall I now re - late What has brought me to this state?

De - puis que j'ai vu Sil - van - dre Me re - gar - der d'un oeil ten - dre,
Ev - er since a shep-herd lad —— Looked at me, my heart is glad, ——

Mon coeur dit à chaque ins - tant: Peut-on vi - vre sans a - mant?
And it tells me with a sigh With-out love I'll sure-ly die!

70

2. In the glen the other day
   He made me a fine bouquet,
   Then he held my shepherd's crook,
   Fixing me with loving look,
   Told me Spring and I compare,
   But to him I am more fair!

3. Then I blushed and was dismayed
   When a sigh my heart betrayed.
   Then that cruel one, with finesse,
   Profited from my weakness.
   One false step, alas 'twas all,
   In his arms then I did fall.

4. I had only for support
   Nothing much of any sort:
   Love did want to have its way,
   Took my crook and dog away.
   Life tastes sweet in every part
   When love takes hold of the heart!

# You, You, in My Heart Living

## (DU, DU, LIEGST MIR IM HERZEN)

English version by Freda Morrill Abrams

German song

*Du,        du*
You,        you,

*liegst mir im Herz - en, Du,        du,        liegst mir im Sinn;*
in   my heart liv -      ing, You,        you,        in my thoughts too,

Du,      du,      machst mir viel Schmer-zen, Weisst nicht wie gut ich dir
You,     you,     joy and pain giv - ing, Don't you know how I   love

bin! _____   Ja,      ja,      ja,
you! _____   You,     you,     you,

ja,      Weisst nich wie gut ich dir bin. _____
you!     Don't you know how I love you! _____

2. You, you have my devotion,
   You, you, give yours to me!
   Oh, oh, fondest emotion
   I feel for you tenderly.
     You, you, you, you!
      I feel for you tenderly.

3. Still, still, won't you be showing
   Some, some sign you are true?
   Why not trust in me knowing
   How good I am, dear, to you!
     You, you, you, you!
      How good I am, dear, to you!

4. If in dreams someday clearly
   To you my face appears,
   Then, then, may Love so dearly
   Unite us all through the years.
     Love, love, love, love,
      Unite us all through the years.

# Oh, Dear!

# What Can the Matter Be?

English song

Not too fast

Oh, dear! What can the matter be?

Dear, dear! What can the matter be? Oh, dear!

What can the mat - ter be? John - ny's so long at the fair.

1. He prom - ised he'd buy me a fair - ing should please me, And
2. He prom - ised he'd bring me a bas - ket of pos - ies, A

then for a kiss, oh, he vowed he would tease me; He
gar - land of lil - ies, a gar - land of ros - es, A

prom - ised he'd buy me a bunch of blue rib - bons, To
lit - tle straw hat to set off the blue rib - bons, That

tie up my bon-nie brown hair.

tie up my bon-nie brown hair.

Oh, dear! What can the mat-ter be? Dear, dear!

What can the mat-ter be? Oh, dear! What can the mat-ter be?

John-ny's so long at the fair.

# Down by the Salley Gardens

W. B. Yeats

1. It was down by the sal - ley gar - dens My love and I did
2. In a field by the riv - er My love and I did

meet. She passed the sal - ley gar - dens With
stand, And on my lean - ing shoul - der She

lit - tle snow - white feet. She bid me take love
placed her snow - white hand; She bid me take life

eas- y, As the leaves grow_ on_ the_ tree, But_
eas- y, As the grass grows_ on_ the_ weirs, But_

I be-ing young and foolish With her did not a-gree.
I was young and foolish And now am full of tears.

*poco rit.*

79

# Were I a Little Bird

## (DER FLUG DER LIEBE)

English version by Freda Morrill Abrams

German song

Simply

Wenn ich ein Vög - lein wär' und auch zwei Flüg - lein hätt',
Were I a lit - tle bird, Had I two lit - tle wings,

flüg' ich zu dir; weil's a - ber nicht kann sein,
To you I'd fly. But since it can - not be,

weil's a - ber nicht kann sein, bleib' ich all - hier.
But since it can - not be, Here then am I.

2. Though I am far from you,
   In dreams I'm near to you,
   Talking with you;
   If I awaken, then,
   If I awaken, then,
   I am alone.

3. No night hour passes by
   That I don't wake and lie
   Thinking of you,
   How you have given me,
   How you have given me,
   Your heart so true.

# Paper of Pins

American song

*Simply*

1. I'll give to you a pa - per of pins, For
2. I'll not ac - cept your pa - per of pins, That's

that's the way our love be - gins, If you will mar - ry
not the way my love be - gins And I'll not mar - ry

me, me, me, If you will mar - ry me. _____
you, you, you, And I'll not mar - ry you. _____

3. I'll give to you a dress of red,
   Stitched all around with a golden thread,
   If you will marry me, me, me,
   If you will marry me.

4. I'll not accept your dress of red,
   Stitched all around with a golden thread,
   And I'll not marry you, you, you,
   And I'll not marry you.

5. I'll give to you my hand and heart
   That we might marry and never part,
   If you will marry me, me, me,
   If you will marry me.

6. I'll not accept your hand and heart
   That we might marry and never part,
   And I won't marry you, you, you,
   And I won't marry you.

7. Now, you love coffee and I love tea,
   You love my money, but you don't love me,
   And I'll not marry you, you, you,
   And I'll not marry you.

8. Oh, then I'll be a withered old maid
   And take my stool and sit in the shade,
   If you'll not marry me, me, me,
   If you'll not marry me.

# LEEZIE LINDSAY

Scottish song

*Freely*

1. Will ye gang to the Hie - lan's, Lee - zie Lind - say? Will ye
2. To _ gang to the Hie - lan's wi' _ you, sir, I _

gang    to    the    Hie - lan's    wi'    me?    Will    ye    gang    to    the
din - na    ken    how    that    may    be,    For    I    ken    na'    the

Hie - lan's, Lee - zie    Lind - say,    My    bride    and    my    dar - ling    to __    be? _____
lan'    that    ye __    live    in,    Nor    ken    I    the    lad    I'm    gaun __    wi'. _____

3. O Leezie, lass, ye maun ken little
   If sae be that ye dinna ken me,
   My name is Lord Ronald MacDonald,
   A chieftan o' high degree.

4. She has kilted her coats o' green satin,
   She has kilted them up to the knee,
   And she's aff wi' Lord Ronald MacDonald,
   His bride an' his darlin' to be.

# Sweet Genevieve

George Cooper

Henry Tucker

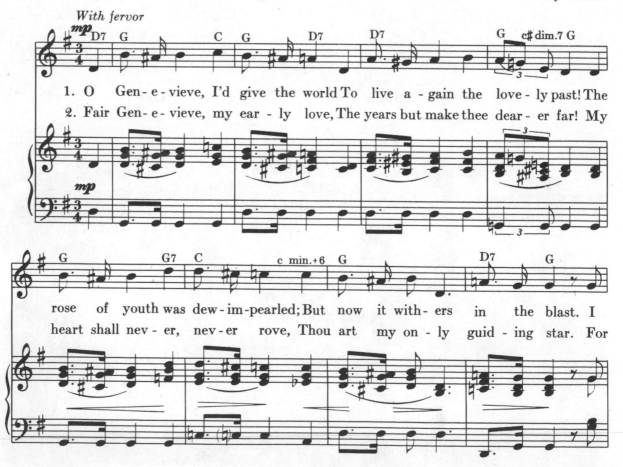

1. O Gen-e-vieve, I'd give the world To live a-gain the love-ly past! The
2. Fair Gen-e-vieve, my ear-ly love, The years but make thee dear-er far! My

rose of youth was dew-im-pearled; But now it with-ers in the blast. I
heart shall nev-er, nev-er rove, Thou art my on-ly guid-ing star. For

87

# LISETTE

English version by Freda Morrill Abrams                                    French song

*En me-nant paî-tre*
As off to pas-ture

*mon trou - peau     Je   vis dans un  bo - ca - ge*
I    did   go,        Lead-ing my flock a - walk -      ing,

*Un ber - ger de no - tre ha - meau, Qui te - nait ce lan-*
I  heard a  shep-herd lad  I     know From our own ham - let ___

89

*poco rit.*  E7  a min.  *Chorus* a tempo  g min.  g min.7  C

ga - ge:  "Li - sette est fai - te pour char - mer,
talk - ing:  "Li - sette is set on earth to charm,

a min.  g min.  g min.7  C7  *f* F  a min.  g min.

Mais en vain je sou - pi - re.  Ah!  qu'on est
But I must sigh so vain - ly.  Ah!  Ah, how

a min.  C7  d min.  F7  g min.  d min.  g min.7  C7  F

mal - heu - reux, Quand on n'o - se le ___ di - re!"
sad am I, I dare not tell her ___ plain - ly!"

2. Her skin is like the lily white,
   Her cheeks are blooming roses,
   Her lips with winning charm delight,
   And grace with her reposes.

3. Her glance sends out a thousand rays,
   Which suddenly enflame me,
   Sure Love is harbored in her eyes
   To overcome and tame me!

CHORUS
"Lisette is set on earth to charm,
But I must sigh so vainly.
Ah! Ah, how sad am I,
I dare not tell her plainly!"

90

# I'll Take You Home Again, Kathleen

Thomas P. Westendorf

1. I'll take you home a - gain, Kath-leen,_____ A-
2. I know you love me, Kath-leen, dear,_____ Your

cross the o - cean wild and wide _____ To where your heart has ev - er
heart was ev - er fond and true; _____ I al - ways feel when you are

been _____ Since first you were my bon-ny bride._____ The
near, That life holds noth-ing dear but you._____ The

where your heart will feel no pain,_____ And when the fields are fresh and

green,_____ I'll __ take you to your home a - gain._____

3. To that dear home beyond the sea,
   My Kathleen shall again return,
   And when thy old friends welcome thee,
   Thy loving heart will cease to yearn.
   Where laughs the little silver stream,
   Beside your mother's humble cot,
   And brightest rays of sunshine gleam,
   There all your grief will be forgot.

   CHORUS

   Oh! I will take you back, Kathleen,
   To where your heart will feel no pain,
   And when the fields are fresh and green,
   I'll take you to your home again.

# When the Corn Is Waving, Annie Dear

Words and music by Charles Blamphin

*With moderate motion*

1. When the corn is wav-ing, An-nie dear, O meet me by the stile, To
2. When the corn is wav-ing, An-nie dear, Our tales of love we'll tell, Be-

hear thy gen - tle voice a - gain And greet thy win - ning smile. The
side the gen - tle flow - ing stream That both our hearts know well. Where

moon will be at full, love, The stars will bright - ly gleam, O
wild flow'rs in their beau - ty Will scent the eve - ning breeze, O

come, my Queen of Night, love, And ___ grace the beau - teous scene. When the
haste, the stars are peep - ing And the moon's be - hind the trees. When the

corn is wav - ing, An - nie dear, O meet me by the stile, To
corn is wav - ing, An - nie dear, Our tales of love we'll tell, Be -

hear thy gen - tle voice a - gain And greet thy win - ning smile.
side the gen - tle flow - ing stream That both our hearts know well.

95

# It's Very True

## (L'È BEN VER)

English version by Freda Morrill Abrams

Song from Friuli region of Italian Alps

*Not too fast*

L'è ben ver, l'è ben ver ch'jo mi slon - ta - - ni
I am far from my home but not my sweet - - heart.

Dal pa - is, dal pa - is ma no del cur.____
I am far, far a - way it's ve - ry true.____

*sempre staccato*

*a tempo*

*poco rit.*

*simile*

Sta pur sal - de, sta pur sal - da, tu ni - ni - ne,
Faith - ful be, oh faith - ful be, my lit - tle dar - ling,

Che jo tor - ni, che jo tor - ni se no mur! tor - ni se no mur!
If I do not die I'll come a - gain to you! see you, dear, once more!

2. Far away are the mountains of my yearning,
   Far away is the girl that I adore,
   There my dreaming, there my dreaming thoughts are turning,
   Sweetest darling, oh to see you, dear, once more!

97

# Skip to My Lou

American song

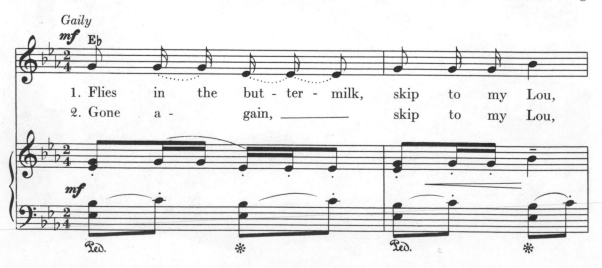

*Gaily*

1. Flies in the but - ter - milk, skip to my Lou,
2. Gone a - gain, _____ skip to my Lou,

Flies in the but-ter-milk, skip to my Lou, Flies in the but-ter-milk,
Gone a- gain, _____ skip to my Lou, Gone a- gain, _____

skip to my Lou, Skip to my Lou, my dar- ling.
skip to my Lou, Skip to my Lou, my dar- ling.

3. Stole my partner, skip to my Lou,
   Stole my partner, skip to my Lou,
   Stole my partner, skip to my Lou,
   Skip to my Lou, my darling.

4. I'll get another one prettier than you,
   I'll get another one prettier than you,
   I'll get another one prettier than you,
   Skip to my Lou, my darling.

5. Chicken on the haystack, shoo, shoo, shoo,
   Chicken on the haystack, shoo, shoo, shoo,
   Chicken on the haystack, shoo, shoo, shoo,
   Skip to my Lou, my darling.

# Ah! Lovely Lady

(¡AY! LINDA AMIGA)

English version by Freda Morrill Abrams

Spanish song

¡Ay! lin-da a-mi-ga, que no vuel-vo a ver-te: Cuer-po ga-
Ah! Love-ly la-dy, to see thee I sigh now, Fig-ure so

rri-do, que me lle-va la muer-te. No hay a-mor sin pe-na,
grace-ful that with-out thee I die now. No love with-out grief and

Pe-na sin do-lor. Ni do-lor tan a-gu-do Co-mo el del a-
No grief with-out woe. There's none so keen a sor-row As the love I

mor. Ni do - lor tan a - gu - do Co - mo el del a - mor.
know, There's none so keen a sor - row As the love I know.

# Comin' thro' the Rye

Robert Burns

1. Gin a bod-y meet a bod-y, Com-in' thro' the rye,
2. Gin a bod-y meet a bod-y, Com-in' frae the toon,

Gin a bod-y kiss a bod-y, Need a bod-y cry?
Gin a bod-y greet a bod-y, Need a bod-y froon? A-

Il - ka las - sie has her lad - die, Nane, they say, hae_ I, Yet
mang the train there is a swain I dear - ly lo'e my - sel'. But

a' the lads they smile at me, When com - in' thro' the rye.
what's his name, or what's his hame, I dan - na care to tell.

# The Rose of Tralee

Irish song

*Andante con moto*

1. The pale moon was ris-ing a-bove the green moun-tain, The
2. The cool shades of eve-ning their man-tle were spread-ing, And

sun was de-clin-ing be-neath the blue sea, __ When I
Ma-ry all smil-ing was lis-tening to me, __ The __

strayed with my love to the pure crys-tal foun-tain That
moon through the val-ley her pale rays was shed-ding, When

stands in the beau-ti-ful vale of Tra-lee.__ She was
I won the heart of the Rose of Tra-lee.__ Though__

love-ly and fair as the rose of __ the __ sum-mer, Yet

'twas not her beau - ty a - lone that won me. O,

no! 'twas the truth in her eye ev - er dawn - ing, That

made me love Ma - ry, the Rose of Tra - lee.

# I Know My Love

Irish song

1. "I know my love by his way o' walk-in', And I know my love by his way o' talk-in', And I know my love in a suit o' blue, And if my love leaves me what will I do-o-o?"

2. "There is a dance-house in Ma-ra-dyke,— And— there my true love goes ev'-ry night.— He— takes a strange one up-on his knee, And— don't you think now that vex-es me-e-e?" And

From *Songs My True Love Sings* by Beatrice Landeck; copyright MCMXLVI by Edward B. Marks Music Corporation. Used by permission.

still she cried, "I love him the best, And a troub-led mind, sure, can

know no rest."— And still she cried, "Bon-ny boys are few, And if

my love leaves me, what will I do?"

3. "If my love knew I could wash and wring,
  If my love knew I could weave and spin,
  I'd make a coat all of the finest kind,
  But the want of money, sure, laves me behind."

CHORUS

And still she cried, "I love him the best,
And a troubled mind, sure, can know no rest."
And still she cried, "Bonny boys are few,
And if my love laves me what will I do?"

# CIELITO LINDO

English version by Freda Morrill Abrams

Mexican song

De la Sie - rra Mo - re - na, Cie - li - to Lin-do, vie -
From la Sier - ra Mo - re - na, Cie - li - to Lin-do, From

- nen ba - jan - do _____ Un par de o _ ji - tos ne - gros, Cie-
_____ high de-scend-ing, _____ Dark eyes so _ black, be-guil- ing, Cie-

- li - to Lin - do, de _____ con - tra - ban - do. _____
- li - to Lin - do, mis - chief pre - tend-ing. _____

110

Ay, ay, ay, ay! _____ Can-
Ay, ay, ay, ay! _____ Sing,

ta y no llo-res _____ por-que can-tan- do se a-
sor- row nev-er! _____ Our hearts__ are joy-ful with

le-gran, Cie- li-to Lin-do los__ co-ra-zo-nes. _____
sing-ing, Cie- li-to Lin-do, sing__ on for-ev-er! _____

2. Fast through the air Love's arrow, Cielito Lindo,
   Comes swiftly playing,
   In my heart strikes his arrow,
   Cielito Lindo, wounding and slaying.

   CHORUS
   Ay, ay, ay, ay!
   Sing, sorrow never!
   Our hearts are joyful with singing,
   Cielito Lindo, sing on forever!

# Drink to Me
## Only with Thine Eyes

Ben Jonson

*Andante, con moto*

1. Drink to me on - ly with thine eyes_ And I _ will pledge with mine; _
2. I sent thee late a ros - y wreath, Not so_much hon - 'ring thee

Or leave a kiss with-in_ the cup, And I'll_ not ask for wine;_ The
As giv - ing it a hope_ that there It could not with-ered be; _ But

From *Fireside Book of Folk Songs*, copyright 1947 by Simon and Schuster, Inc., and Artists and Writers Guild, Inc.

thirst that from the soul doth rise, Doth ask a drink divine;
thou there-on did'st only breathe, And sent'st it back to me,

But might I of Jove's nectar sup, I would not change for thine.
Since when it grows and smells, I swear, Not of itself but thee.

# Kathleen Mavourneen

Mrs. Crawford

F. Nicholls Crouch

1. Kath - leen Ma - vour - neen! The grey dawn is break-ing,__ The
2. Kath - leen Ma - vour - neen! A - wake from thy slum-bers, _ The

horn of the hun - ter is _ heard __ on the hill; The
blue moun-tains glow in the_ sun's __ gold-en light; Ah!

lark from her light wing the bright dew is shak - ing, —
Where is the spell that once hung on my num - bers? A -

Kath - leen Ma-vour-neen! What, slum - b'ring still? Oh,
rise in thy beau-ty, thou star of my night. Ma-

hast thou for-got-ten how soon we must sev-er? Oh,
vour - neen, Ma-vour-neen, my sad tears are fal-ling, To

hast thou for-got-ten this day we must part?
think that from E - rin and thee I must part,

It
To

# CARMELA

English version by Olcutt Sanders

Spanish-American song

With easy motion

A - sí cual mue-ren en oc - ci - den- te Los ti - bios ra - vos del as - tro
As die at ev'-ning on far ho - ri -zons The last faint rays of the sov'-reign

rey,
light,

A - sí mu - rie - ron mís i - lu -
So die with- in me my fond il -

sio - nes, A - sí ex - tin - guién-do - se va mí fé.
lu - sions, So fades my faith in - to black - est night.

# Ca' the Ewes

Words by Robert Burns

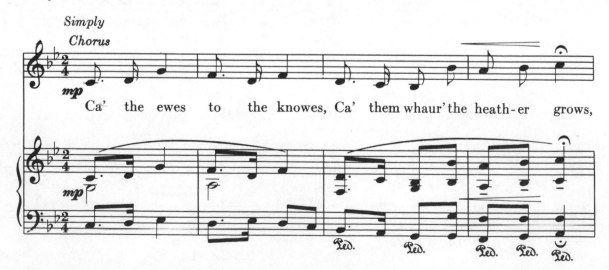

*Simply*

*Chorus*

*mp*

Ca' the ewes to the knowes, Ca' them whaur'the heath-er grows,

Ca' them whaur' the burn-ie rows, My bon-nie dear-ie.

1. Hark, the mav-is ev'n-in' song, Sound-in' Clu-den's woods a - mang,
2. We'll gae down by Clu - den side, Through the ha-zels spread-ing wide,

Then a-fauld-in' let us gang, My ____ bon-nie dear-ie.
O'er the waves that sweet-ly glide, To the moon sae clear-ly.

3. Fair and lovely as thou art,
Thou hast stown my very heart:
I can die, but canna part,
My bonnie dearie.

CHORUS

Ca' the ewes to the knowes,
Ca' them whaur' the heather grows,
Ca' them whaur' the burnie rows,
My bonnie dearie.

*Note:* ca'— call; knowes—knolls; burnie—brooklet;
rows—rolls; a-fauldin—sheep folding; sae—so.

# Say "Au Revoir" but Not "Good-bye"

Words and music by Harry Kennedy

*Moderately fast*

1. Say "au re - voir" _____ but not "good-bye," _____ For part- ing
2. The call has come, _____ I'm off to war, _____ Midst crash of

brings _____ a bit- ter sigh, _____ My coun-try needs _____ me in this
shell _____ and can- non roar, _____ The past has gone, _____ tho' mem-ory

122

fight \_\_\_\_ For free - dom, lib - er - ty and right. \_\_\_\_ Our du - ty
gives \_\_\_\_ One cling-ing thought \_\_\_ the fu - ture lives; \_\_\_\_ This one good-

first, \_\_\_\_ love must not lead, \_\_\_ What might have been \_\_\_\_ had fate de -
bye \_\_\_\_ may be our last, \_\_\_ The word is spoke, \_\_ the die is

creed; _____ I'll ne'er for - get _____ the day we
cast, _____ But still my heart _____ beats wild with

met, \_\_\_ I loved you then, \_\_\_ I love you yet. \_\_\_
pain, \_\_\_ And though we may \_\_\_ not meet a - gain: \_\_\_

# Far Is My Love

## (TUOLL' ON MUN KULTANI)

English version by Freda Morrill Abrams

Finnish song

*Freely, with melancholy*

Tuoll' on mun kul - ta - ni, ain' y - hä tuol - la,
1. Far is my love, to the cas - tle he's tak - en,
2. O for the day we'll be once more to - geth - er,

ku - nin - kaan kul - tai - sen kar - ta - non puol - la. Voi mi - nun lin - tu - ni,
Serv - ing the king, leav - ing me here for - sak - en. O lit - tle dove of mine,
Most joy - ful day that u - nites us for - ev - er! O dear - est love of mine,

voi mi - nun kul - ta - ni, kun et tu - le jo, kun et tu - le jo!
Come a - gain to me, come a - gain to me!

# ANNIE LAURIE

William Douglas

*Not too slowly*

1. Max - wel - ton's braes are bon - nie, Where ear - ly fa's ___ the
2. Her ___ brow is like the snaw-drift, Her throat is like ___ the

dew, And it's there that An - nie Lau - rie Gave
swan, Her ___ face it is the fair - est That

me her prom - ise true. Gave me her prom - ise
e'er the sun shone on. That e'er the sun shone

true, Which ne'er for - got will be, }
on, And dark blue is her e'e, }

And for

bon - nie An - nie Lau-rie___ I'd__ lay__ me doon and dee.

3. Like dew on the gowan lying,
   Is the fa' o' her fairy feet,
   And like winds in summer sighing,
   Her voice is low and sweet.
   Her voice is low and sweet,
   And she's a' the world to me,
   And for bonnie Annie Laurie
   I'd lay me doon and dee.

# My Luve Is Like

## a Red, Red Rose

Robert Burns

*With fervor*

1. O, my luve is like a red, red rose, That's new-ly sprung in June; O, my luve is like a mel-o-die That's sweet-ly played in tune! As fair art thou, my bon-nie lass, So

2. Till a' the seas gang dry, my dear, And the rocks melt wi' the sun; And I will luve thee still, my dear, While the sands of life shall run. But, fare thee weel, my on-ly luve! O

128

deep in luve am I;___ And __ I will luve thee still, my dear, Till
fare thee weel a - while!_ And __ I will come a - gain, my luve, Tho'

a' the seas gang dry. Till a' the seas gang dry, my dear, Till
'twere ten thou-sand mile. Tho' 'twere ten thou-sand mile, my luve, Tho'

a' the seas gang dry; And ___ I will luve thee still, my dear, Till
'twere ten thou-sand mile, And ___ I will come a - gain, my luve, Tho'

a' the seas gang dry.
'twere ten thou - sand mile.

# DARK EYES

(OCHY CHORNIA)

English version by Carol Raven

Russian song

2. Eyes so dark and bright,
   Light my way tonight,
   Into lands of love,
   Where we'll find delight,
   Where all sorrow is gone,
   Where love reigns alone,
   Where I'll be with you,
   Eyes of fire and dew!

# While Strolling through the Park

Ed. Haley

While stroll-ing thro'the park one day, In the mer-ry month of

May,___ I was tak-en by sur-prise by a pair of ro-guish eyes, In a

mo-ment my poor heart was stole a-way.___ A smile was all she

# Lumberman's Song

## (MINUM KULTANI)

English version by Freda Morrill Abrams

Finnish song

*Vivace*

Mi - nun kul - ta - ni kau - nis on, vaikk' on kai - ta -
My sweet - heart is a gor - geous gal, Tho' she's thin and

lui - nen; Mi - nun kul - ta - ni kau - nis on,
bon - y; My sweet - heart is a gor - geous gal,

*f Chorus*

vaikk' on kai - ta - lui - nen. Hei luu - li - a, il - lal - la,
Tho' she's thin and bon - y. Hey loo - lee - a, tra - la - la,

vaikk' on kai - ta - lui - nen, hei luu - li - a,
Tho' she's thin and bon - y, Hey loo - lee - a,

*poco rit.*     *a tempo*

il - lal - la, vaikk' on kai - ta - lui - nen.
tra - la - la, Tho' she's thin and bon - y.

*(Repeat each verse and each chorus once)*

2. My gal's head is small and neat
   Tho' it's slightly crooked.
   *Chorus:* Hey loo-lee-a, tra-la-la,
          Tho' it's slightly crooked.

3. My gal's hair is dark, dark brown,
   But she never combs it.
   *Chorus:* Hey loo-lee-a, tra-la-la,
          But she never combs it.

4. My sweetheart has bright blue eyes,
   But they cross each other.
   *Chorus:* Hey loo-lee-a, tra-la-la,
          But they cross each other.

5. My loved one has a pretty mouth,
   Ear to ear it stretches.
   *Chorus:* Hey loo-lee-a, tra-la-la,
          Ear to ear it stretches.

6. Oh, I'm not afraid of her
   Though she's two times bigger.
   *Chorus:* Hey loo-lee-a, tra-la-la,
          Though she's two times bigger.

7. When we go to the market-place
   Horses start in laughing.
   *Chorus:* Hey loo-lee-a, tra-la-la,
          Horses start in laughing.

# I Know Where I'm Goin'

Irish song

1. I know where __ I'm go - in', _____ And
2. I have stock-ings of silk, _____

3. Some say he's black,
   But I say he's bonny,
   The fairest of them all,
   My handsome, winsome Johnny.

4. Feather beds are soft,
   And painted rooms are bonny,
   But I would leave them all
   To go with my love Johnny.

5. I know where I'm goin',
   And I know who's goin' with me,
   I know who I love,
   But the dear knows who I'll marry!

# LITTLE KAREN

### (HUSKER DU I HOEST)

Parmo Carl Ploug

English version by Freda Morrill Abrams

P. Heise

*Andante*

Hu - sker du i Hoest, da vi hjem-ad fra Mar-ken gik,
D'you re - call, in Au - tumn, when home from the fair we went,

vend - te du i - mod mig et spoer - gen-de Blik;
When your eyes met mine, then a question-ing look they sent?

da faldt det mig paa Sind,____ at jeg var_ hid - til blind.
There came in - to my mind ___ That hith- er-to I'd been blind,

A7    d min.    A7    d min.    G    G7    C

*Sig mig, lil - le Ka - ren, hvad men - te du da?*
Tell me, lit - tle Ka - ren, what were you think - ing then,

Cmaj.7    F    a min.    e min.    F    C    G7    C

*mf*
*slower*
*Sig mig, lil - le Ka - ren, hvad men - te du da?*
Tell me, lit - tle Ka - ren, what were you think - ing then?

*mf*
*slower*

2. D'you recall, in Winter, we sat by the fireplace,
   I told of adventure, but seeing your dear face
   I had to stop, you see,
   When you looked up at me,
   Tell me, little Karen, what were you thinking then,
   Tell me, little Karen, what were you thinking then?

3. D'you remember Christmas, the dancing and flutes that played,
   O'er the floor together so merrily we swayed,
   I looked so long at you
   You blushed a crimson hue,
   Tell me, little Karen, what were you thinking then,
   Tell me, little Karen, what were you thinking then?

4. See, it is the Spring now, and birds are all building nests,
   Flower buds are op'ning, the trees in bridal dress,
   All of Life seems to sing,
   Dreaming of Love and Spring,
   Tell me, little Karen, what are you thinking now,
   Tell me, little Karen, what are you thinking now?

# When the Cock Crows

### (AL CHANTE IL GIAL)

English version by Freda Morrill Abrams

Italian song

Al chan-te il gial    Al cri-che il di    Cha - re mo -
When the cock crows    At break of day,    Dear - est be -

ro - se  Mi to - ce a  par - ti.    E vè o par-tis,    Do - man soi
lov - ed,  I  must go a - way.    Yes, I must go,    Soon comes the

vi - e, *Con - so - la - mi, Con - so - la - mi, E vè o par-*
mor - row, Con - sole me now, Con - sole me now. Yes, I must

tis, ___ *Do - man soi vi - e, Con - so - la - mi, A far l'a - mor!*
go, ___ Soon comes the mor - row, Con - sole me now with love, with love!

# The Last Rose of Summer

Thomas Moore

*Slowly and freely*

1. 'Tis the last rose_ of_ sum-mer, Left_ bloom-ing a- lone, All her
2. I'll not leave thee, thou_ lone one, To_ pine_____ on the stem. Since the

*With pedal*

love - ly_ com- pan -ions Are_ fa - ded and_ gone. No_
love - ly_ are_ sleep-ing, Go_ sleep _____ thou with them. Thus_

flow - er of her kin - dred, No_ rose - bud is nigh_____ To re-
kind - ly I _ scat- ter Thy_ leaves_ o'er the bed, _____ When thy

*slower and softer a tempo*

142

flect back ___ her ___ blush - es    Or ___ give _____ sigh for sigh.
mates of ___ the ___ gar - den    Lie ___ scent - _____ less   and dead.

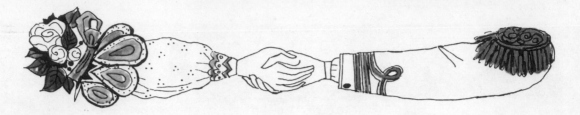

# My Bonnie Lies over the Ocean

Words and music by Charles E. Pratt

1. My bon - nie lies o - ver the o - cean,___ While sad - ly I
He comes to my heart in bright vis - ions,___ His face like an

wait on the shore,_____ He wan - dered a - way o'er the
an - gel's I see,_____ And still do I sigh in my

bil - lows,___ I'm long - ing to see him once more.___
dream - ing,___ Oh! bring back my bon - nie to me.___

Bring back, bring back, Bring back my love o'er the sea, the sea; Bring back, bring back, Oh! bring back my bon-nie to me.

2. He left me when roses were fading,
   To bid me farewell for a while;
   My heart is so weary and lonely,
   Bereft of his beautiful smile.
   I stay where the billows are dashing
   And wonder where now he can be,
   My heart to the waves ever whispers,
   Oh! Bring back my bonnie to me.

3. Then, darling one, can you forsake me?
   My life is so weary and lone!
   Oh! Send me a word o'er the water,
   And say that you're ever my own.
   In sorrow and tears I'm repining,
   And sad is my watch by the sea,
   My darling, my dear one forever,
   Oh! Bring back my bonnie to me.

CHORUS
Bring back, bring back,
Bring back my love o'er the sea, the sea,
Bring back, bring back,
Oh! Bring back my bonnie to me.

# TUM-BALALAYKA

Israeli song

Lyrics (voice line):

*Shteyt a bo-cher un__ er tracht Tracht un tracht a gan-tse nacht: Ve-men tsu ne-men un nit far-she-men? Ve-men tsu ne-men un nit far-she-men?*

A lad stood think-ing all the night through, Think-ing, think-ing what_ to do. Whose heart to take? Whose heart not to break? Whose heart __ to take? Whose heart not to break? ___

2. Maiden, maiden, tell me true,
   What can grow, grow without dew?
   What can burn for years and years?
   What can cry and shed no tears?

3. Silly lad, here's the answer true:
   A stone can grow, grow without dew.
   Love can burn for years and years.
   A heart can cry and shed no tears.

**CHORUS**
Tum-bala, tum-bala, tum-balalayka,
Tum-bala, tum-bala, tum-balalayka,
Tum-balalayka, shpil balalayka,
Tum-balalayka, shpil balalayka.

149

# The Turtle Dove

English song

*Allegro moderato*

1. Fare you well, my dear, I must be __ gone, And __ leave you __ for a __
2. So __ fair thou art, my bon - nie __ lass, So __ deep in __ love am __

while; If I roam___ a - way I'll___ come___ back a-gain, Though I
I; But I nev-er will prove false to the bon-nie lass I love Till the

roam ten thou-sand miles, my dear, Though I roam ten thou - sand miles.
stars fall from the sky, my dear, Till the stars fall from the sky.

3. The sea will never run dry, my dear,
   Nor the rocks never melt with the sun,
   But I never will prove false to the bonnie lass I love
   Till all these things be done, my dear,
   Till all these things be done.

4. O yonder doth sit that little turtle dove,
   He doth sit on yonder high tree,
   A-making a moan for the loss of his love,
   As I will do for thee, my dear,
   As I will do for thee.

# Prithee, Pretty Maiden

From *"Patience"*

Sir William Schwenck Gilbert

Sir Arthur Seymour Sullivan

*Allegretto*

1. Pri - thee, pret - ty maid - en,
2. Gen - tle sir, my heart is

pri - thee tell me true,   (Hey, but I'm dole - ful, wil - low, wil - low wa - ly!)
frol - ic - some and free,   (Hey, but he's dole - ful, wil - low, wil - low wa - ly!)

Have you e'er a lov - er a - dan - gling af - ter you?
No - bod - y I care for comes a - court - ing me.

Hey, wil-low wa-ly o! I would fain dis-cov-er,
Hey, wil-low wa-ly o! No-bod-y I care for

if you have a lov-er Hey — wil-low wa-ly — o!
comes a-court-ing, there-fore, Hey, — wil-low wa-ly — o!

3. Prithee, pretty maiden, will you marry me?
   (Hey, but I'm hopeful, willow, willow waly!)
   I may say at once I'm a man of propertee,
   Hey, willow waly o!
   Money, I despise it, but many people prize it,
   Hey, willow waly o!

4. Gentle sir, altho to marry I design,
   (Hey, but he's hopeful, willow, willow waly!)
   Yet I do not know you, and so I must decline,
   Hey, willow waly o!
   To other maidens go you, as yet I do not know you,
   Hey, willow waly o!

# SONGS FROM THE GREAT COMPOSERS

# ICH LIEBE DICH

## (I LOVE YOU)

Herrossee
Translation by Hedi Salzer
Versification by Freda Morrill Abrams

Ludwig van Beethoven

*Andante sostenuto*

Ich lie - be dich, so wie du mich, am A - bend und am Mor - gen, noch
As I love thee, so you love me At ev'-ning, morn-ing, car - ing, There's

war kein Tag, wo du und ich nicht teil - ten un - s're Sor - gen.
nev - er been a day when we Our bur -dens were not shar - ing.

Auch war - en sie für dich und mich ge -
Our cares much light- er seem to be When

157

teilt leicht zu _ er - tra - gen; du trös - te - test im Kum-mer mich, ich _
we each oth - er's _ bor - row, If I am sad, you com - fort me, I _

weint' in dei - ne Kla - gen, in dei - ne Kla - gen. D'rum
weep when you have sor - row, When you have sor - row. And _

Got - tes Seg - en ü - ber dir, du mei - nes Le - bens Freu - de, Gott
so may God his bless - ing lay On thee, my joy of liv - ing, May

schüt - ze dich, er - halt' dich mir, schütz' und er - halt' _ uns _ bei - de, Gott
God watch o'er us both, I pray, His ben - e - dic - tion _ giv - ing, May

schüt- ze dich, er-halt' dich mir, schütz' und er-halt' uns
God watch o'er us both, I pray, His ben-e-dic-tion

bei-de, er-halt', er-halt' uns bei-de, er-halt' uns
giv-ing, His ben-e-dic-tion giv-ing, Ben-e-dic-tion

bei - de!
giv - ing.

# Aus meinen grossen Schmerzen

(OUT OF MY SOUL'S GREAT SADNESS)

Heinrich Heine
Translation by Hedi Salzer
Versification by Freda Morrill Abrams

Robert Franz

*Andante—with fervor*

*mp*

Aus mein-en gro - ssen Schmer - zen   mach' ich die klei - nen
Out   of my soul's great sad - ness,   My   lit - tle songs I'm

*espress.*
*mp dolce*
*Ped.   Ped. Ped.   Ped.   Ped.   simile*

Lie -   der,   die he - ben ihr kling - end Ge - fie -   der   und
sing -   ing,   They rise   on the air,   mu - sic   ring -   ing,   And

*mp*
*pp*

160

flat - tern nach ihr - em Her - - zen. Sie
fly to my love___ with glad - - ness. They're

fan - den den Weg zur Trau - ten, doch kom - men sie wie - der und
waft - ed on wings of yearn - ing, Re - turn - ing they're gen - tly com-

kla - gen, und kla - gen, und wo - llen nicht sa - gen, was
plain - ing, Com - plain - ing yet nev - er ex - plain - ing What

sie __ im Her - zen schau - - ten.
they in her heart are learn - - ing.

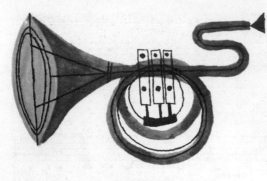

# GENTLE ANNIE

Words and music by Stephen Foster

Andante

*mp*

1. Thou wilt come no more, gen-tle An-nie, Like a
2. We have roamed and loved 'mid the bow-ers, When thy

flow'r thy spi-rit did de-part; Thou art gone, a-las! like the
dow-ny cheeks were in their bloom; Now I stand a-lone 'mid the

man-y That have bloomed in the Sum-mer of my heart. Shall we
flow-ers, While they min-gle their per-fumes o'er thy tomb.

Chorus

nev-er more be-hold thee; Nev-er hear thy win-ning voice a-

gain,        When the spring - time    comes, gen - tle   An - nie,            When the

wild        flow'rs are   scat - tered o'er    the    plain?

3. Ah! the hours grow sad while I ponder
    Near the silent spot where thou art laid,
    And my heart bows down when I wander
    By the stream and the meadows where we strayed.

CHORUS

Shall we never more behold thee;
Never hear thy winning voice again,
When the springtime comes, gentle Annie,
When the wild flow'rs are scattered o'er the plain?

# Plaisir d'amour

(THE JOYS OF LOVE)

Jean Paul Martini

Allegretto, con moto

Plai - sir d'a - mour ne
The joys of love are

du - re qu'un mo - ment: cha - grin d'a -
al - ways quick - ly pass - ing, Tor - ment of

*mour du - re tou - te la vi _____*
love, all through life ____ is last - - - - - -

e.
ing.

*J'ai*
My

tout quit - té pour l'in - gra - te Syl - vi - e;
love for faith - less Syl - via now is o - ver.

el - le me quit - te et prend un
She broke with me and took an -

au - tre a - mant.
oth - er lov - er.

Plai - sir d'a - mour ne
The joys of love are

du - re qu'un mo - ment: _____ cha - grin d'a -
al - ways quick - ly pass - ing, Tor - ment of

mour du - re tou - te la _ vi _____
love, all through life _____ is _ last - - - - - -

e.
ing.

poco rit.

"Tant que cet-te eau cou-le-ra_____ dou-ce-
"While there the tran-quil_____ brook-let on-ward

ment_____ vers ce ruis-seau qui bor-de la_____ prai-
flows,_____ While sea-ward flows the brook-let through the

ri-e je t'ai-me-rai,"
mead-ow, I, I will love you."

169

me ré - pé -tait__ Syl - vi - - e.    L'eau    cou - le en-
So said to me,__ my Syl - vi - a.    Still,    on flows the

*dim.*

core,__    el - le a    chan - gé __ pour-tant. __    Plai -
brook __    But Syl - via's love__ is gone. __    The

sir    d'a -    mour __    ne du - re qu'un__ mo -
joys    of    love __    are al - ways quick - ly

ment: __    cha - grin    d'a -
pass - ing,    Tor - ment    of

mour du - re tou - te la vi — — — — — e.
love, all through life __ is last - — — - — ing.

# Chantons les amours de Jean

(OH SING OF THE LOVE OF JOHN)

English version by Freda Morrill Abrams

French song

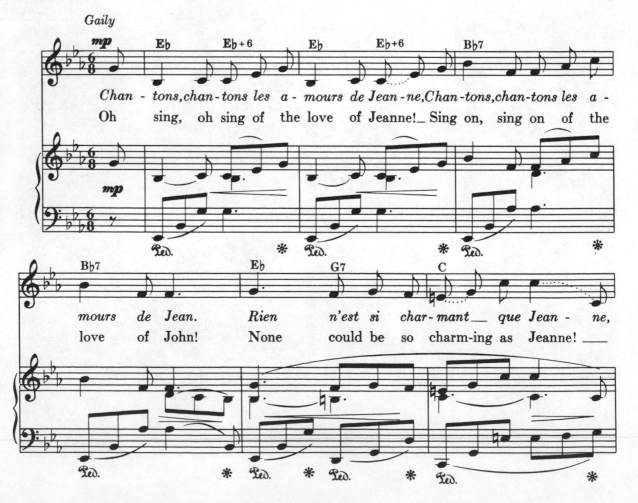

Gaily

Chan - tons, chan - tons les a - mours de Jean - ne, Chan - tons, chan - tons les a -
Oh     sing,  oh sing of  the  love   of Jeanne!_ Sing on,  sing on  of  the

mours   de Jean.     Rien     n'est si  char - mant_  que Jean - ne,
love     of John!    None     could be  so   charm - ing  as  Jeanne!_

Rien plus __ ai - ma - ble que Jean. Jean ai - me Jean - ne,
None could be so gal - lant as John! John __ loves Jeanne, __

Jeanne ai - me Jean, Jean ai - me Jean - ne, Jeanne ai - me jo - li Jean.
Jeanne __ loves John, John __ loves Jeanne, __ Jeanne loves her dar - ling John!

2. Their simple cottage a palace seems,
All made of gold shining in the sun!
There John has the love of Jeanne!
And Jeanne has the love of John!

3. Oh great indeed is the love of Jeanne,
But no less great is the love of John.
Just whatever one wants to do,
Soon the other's wanting it too!

CHORUS:

John loves Jeanne, Jeanne loves John,
John loves Jeanne, Jeanne loves her darling John!

# THE GARLAND

Francis Hopkinson

*Andante grazioso*

The pride of ev'-ry_ grove I_ chose, The vio-let sweet and

li-ly_ fair,_ The dap-pled_pink and blush-ing_ rose, To

deck my_charm-ing Chlo-e's hair! At

morn the _ nymph vouch- safed _ to place  Up - on  her  brow  the

var - ious wreath, _ The flow'rs  less bloom - ing  than  her face, Their _

*poco rit.*                                    *a tempo*

scent less  fra - grant _ than _ her  hair!

*f broadly*

Their _  scent less  fra - grant _ than _____  her  hair!

# Caro mio ben

### (JOY OF MY HEART)

English version by Freda Morrill Abrams

Giuseppe Giordani

Moderato

Ca - ro mio
Joy of my

ben, cre - di - mi al - men, sen - za di te lan - gui-sce il cor, _
heart, When we're a - part I sigh for thee, Sigh _ and a - dore. _

ca - ro mio ben, sen - za di te _ lan - gui - sce il cor.
Joy of my heart, I sigh for thee, Sigh and _ a - dore.

cor, ca - ro mio ben, cre - di - mi al -men, sen - za di
dore. Joy__ of my heart, When__ we're a - part, I sigh for

te _____ lan - gui - sce il cor.
thee, _____ Sigh and a - dore.

# WIDMUNG

## (O THANK ME NOT FOR SONGS I SING THEE)

Wolfgang Müller
Translation by Hedi Salzer
Versification by Freda Morrill Abrams

Robert Franz

*Andante espressivo*

O dan - ke nicht für die - se Lie - der, mir ziemt es
O thank me not for songs I sing you, Rath - er to

*With pedal*

dank - bar Dir zu sein; Du gabst sie mir, ___ ich ge - be
you I'd grate - ful be; You gave them me, ___ I on - ly

wie - der, was jetzt und einst und e - wig Dein.
bring you What is your own e - ter - nal - ly.

*8va*

181

# Thy Beaming Eyes

W. H. Gardner

Edward MacDowell

*With sentiment, passionately*

Thy beam-ing eyes Are Par - a - dise To me, my love, to me. Thy

*loud*

fear. _____ Thy beam - ing eyes Are Par - a - dise To me, my

dear. _____

*as soft as possible*

# The Self-Banished

Edmund Waller

Dr. John Blow

It is not that __ I love you less__ Than when__ be-fore __ your feet I lay; But to pre - vent __ the

sad in - crease of hope-less love I keep a - way.

In vain a - las! for ev - 'ry - thing which I have

known be - long to you, Your form does to my

fan - cy bring And make my old wounds bleed a - new.

# When Laura Smiles

Philip Rosseter

1. When Lau - ra smiles, Her sight re - vives,
The Earth and Heav - en Views with de - light

Both night and day.
Her wan - ton play. And her speech with ev - er -

- flow - ing mu - sicke doth re - paire The cru - el

wounds of sor - row and un - tam'd de - spaire.

2. The Spirits that remaine in floating air
Affect for pastime to untwine her tressed haire.
And the birds think sweete Aurora, morning's Queene, doth shine
From her bright sphere, when Laura shows her looks divine.

3. Diana's eyes are not adorned with greater power
Than Laura's, when she lifts awhile, for sport to loure.
But when she her eyes encloseth, blindnesse doth appeare
The chiefest grace of beautie sweetly sealed there.

# Still wie die Nacht

(STILL AS THE NIGHT)

Translation by Hedi Salzer

Versification by Freda Morrill Abrams

Carl Bohm

Still    wie    die    Nacht,        tief    wie    das Meer,____

Still    as    the    night,        Deep    as    the    sea,____

soll dei - ne Lie - be sein! _____
Should be your love _____ for me. _____

Still wie die Nacht _____ und tief wie das Meer
Still as the night, _____ Deep as the sea,

*col 8va* _ _ _ _ _ _ _ _ _

soll dei - ne Lie - be, dei - ne Lie - be sein, _____
Should be your love, Should be your love _____ for me, _____

*col 8va* _ _ _ _ _ _ _ _ _ _

*poco rit.*      *a tempo*

soll dei - ne Lie - be sein!
Should be your love _____ for me.

*poco rit.*     *a tempo*

Wenn du mich  
If you love  

liebst so wie ich dich, ____ will ich dein  
me, As I love thee, ____ Ev - er your  

ei - gen sein!  
own ____ I'll be.  

Heiss ____ wie der  
Last - ing as  

Stahl ____ und fest wie der Stein soll dei - ne
stone, ____ And glow - ing as steel, Should be your

Lie - be, dei - ne Lie - be sein, ____ soll dei - ne
love, Should be your love ____ for me, ____ Should be your

Lie - be _ sein! ____
love ____ for _ me. ____

# Que ne suis-je la fougère

(MIGHT I BE THE WOODED FERNBRAKE)

French verse by Charles Henri Riboutte

English version by Freda Morrill Abrams

Giovanni Battista Pergolesi

*Que ne suis - je la fou - gè - re où, sur la fin — d'un beau*

Might I be the wood-ed fern - brake At the end of a love - ly

*jour, Se re - po - se ma ber - gè - re, Sous la gar - de de l'a-*

day, Where my shep - herd girl re - pos - es, There doth Love her hom - age

mour! / pay. *Que ne suis - je le zé - phy - re Qui raf* / Could I be the gen - tle zeph - yr Sigh - ing

*fraî - chit ses ap - pas, L'air que sa bou - che res -* / 'round her charms so sweet, Or the air her lips are

*pi - re, La fleur qui naît ___ sous ses pas!* / breath - ing, Or the flow'r spring-ing 'neath her feet!

2. Could I be the purest waters
   Which surround her lovely form—
   After bathing, be her garments
   Which she dons to keep her warm!
      Might I be her glass reflecting
      Her sweet image o'er and o'er,
      To all eyes such grace revealing
      Her great beauty more and more!

3. Could I by some happy dreaming
   Keep her heart enchanted too,
   Might I by some fine illusion
   Make my love dreams all come true!
      For the Gods who set me breathing
      Make me seek the greatest prize,
      For my goal is set at being
      All that's pleasing to her eyes!

# Gather Ye Rosebuds

Robert Herrick

William Lawes

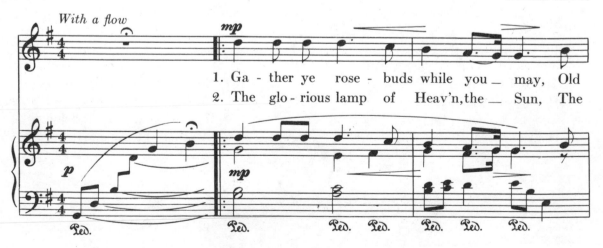

*With a flow*

*mp*

1. Ga - ther ye rose - buds while you _ may, Old
2. The glo - rious lamp of Heav'n, the _ Sun, The

*p*   *mp*

Time is still _ a - fly - ing, And that same flow'r that smiles _ to -
high - er he _ is _ get - ting, The soon-er will his race _ be

day To - mor - row _ will be dy - ing.
run, And near - er _ he's to set - ting.

3. That age is best that is the first
   While youth and blood are warmer;
   But being spent the worse and worst,
   Time still succeeds the former.

4. Then be not coy, but use your time,
   And while you may, go marry,
   For having once but lost your prime,
   You may forever tarry.

# Du bist wie eine Blume

### (YOU ARE SO LIKE A FLOWER)

Heinrich Heine
Translation by Hedi Salzer
Versification by Freda Morrill Abrams

Robert Schumann

Du bist wie ei - ne Blu - me, so
You are so like a flow - er, So

hold und schön und rein; ich schau' dich an, und
fair and pure and kind; I look on you and

Weh - muth schleicht mir in's Herz hin - ein. Mir
long - ing Steals in my heart and mind. My

ist, _____ als ob ich die Hän - de auf's Haupt dir le - gen
hands_____ I would be lay - ing Up - on your head _____ in

sollt', be - tend dass Gott dich er - hal - te
prayer That God will ev - er - more keep you

so rein und schön und hold.
So kind and pure and fair.

199

# Es hat die Rose sich beklagt

(ONE DAY THE LOVELY ROSE COMPLAINED)

Translation by Hedi Salzer
Versification by Freda Morrill Abrams

Robert Franz

*Larghetto—Passionately tender*

Es hat die Ro - se sich __ be-
One day the love - ly rose __ com-

*mf espressivo*

*With pedal*

klagt, __ dass gar zu schnell der Duft ver - ge - he, den ihr der
plained, __ That far too soon was beau - ty dy - ing, And Spring's sweet

Lenz _ ge - ge - ben ha - be.
fra - grance ev - er flee - ing.

Da hab' ich'
Then to con-

ihr zum Trost _ ge - sagt, _ dass er durch mei - ne Lie - der
sole her I _ ex - plained, That these my songs are death de -

we - he, und dort ein ew' - ges Le - ben ha - be.
fy - ing, In them she'll al - ways have her be - ing.

# Occhietti amati

(BELOVED EYES)

English version by Freda Morrill Abrams

Andrea Falconieri

*With passion*

Oc - chiet -ti a - ma - ti    che    m'in - cen - de -    te
Be - lov - ed    eyes, you    so    bright - ly    burn    me,

Per - chè    spie - ta - ti    o - mai    più    sie -    te?
Why, tell    me    why    you    now    cruel - ly    spurn    me?

Splen-dan se - re - ni di gio - ia pie - ni, Splen-dan se -
Shin - ing so keen - ly With joy, se - rene - ly, Shin-ing so

re - ni di gio - ia pie - ni Vo - stri splen-do - ri
keen - ly With joy, se - rene - ly, My heart a - dores thee,

fiam - - - me de' co - ri.
Fired _____ by thy glo - ry! _____

2. Mouth of vermillion, your lips confining
   Wonders a million, pearls, rubies, shining.
   When gently smiling,  } Repeat
   You are beguiling.
   Will passion move you?
   Say that you love, too.

# Die Lotosblume

## (THE LOTUS FLOWER)

Heinrich Heine
Translation by Hedi Salzer
Versification by Freda Morrill Abrams

Robert Schumann

Die Lo - tos - blu - me äng - stigt
The lo - tus flow - er trem - bles,

sich vor der Son - ne Pracht,
Fear - ing the sun so bright,

und mit ge - senk - tem
Bend - ing her head so

Haup - te er - war - tet sie träum - end die Nacht.
hum - bly She dreams as she waits for the night.

Der
The

Mond, der ist ___ ihr Buh - le, er weckt sie mit sei - nem
moon, he is ___ her lov - er, He wakes her with sil - v'ry

Licht, und ihm ent - schlei - ert sie freund - lich ihr
light, To him she glad - ly un - cov - ers Her

*poco a poco accel.*

from - mes Blu - men - ge - sicht. Sie blüht und glüht und
flow - er - face, pure, to his sight. She blooms and glows, and,

*poco a poco accel.*

# DOUCE DAME JOLIE

### (LADY FAIR AND GENTLE)

English version by Lyndal Brandeis

Guillaume de Machault

Douce dame jolie, Pour Dieu ne penses mie
Lady fair and gentle, Never believe, I pray you,

Que nulle ait seignourie Sur moi, fors vous seulement.
That one may have power O'er me, saving you alone.

2. Lady, fair and gentle,
   In all the days of my living
   Have I without deceiving
   Humbly served but you alone.

# Mein Mädel hat einen Rosenmund

(MY MAIDEN'S LIPS ARE LIKE A ROSE)

German folk song
Arranged by Johannes Brahms

English version by Freda Morrill Abrams

Mein Mä - del hat ei - nen Ro - sen-mund und wer ihn küsst, der _ wird ge-sund; O du! O du! O du! O _

My maid-en's lips are _ like a rose, To kiss them, oh such _ joy one knows; My dear! My dear! My dear! Oh _

du schwarz-brau- nes Mäg- de- lein,* du la, la, la, la, la! Du __
my dear dark- eyed Mag-de- line, You la, la, la, la, la! You __

la, la, la, la, la! Du lässt __ mir kei- ne Ruh!
la, la, la, la, la! No peace __ you leave me, dear!

2. Your cheeks are touched by a shining glow,
   Like morning sun on winter snow;
   *Chorus*

3. Your eyes are like the dark of night,
   But sparkling there two stars give light;
   *Chorus*

4. Like cloudless skies of heavenly blue,
   My maiden's heart is good and true;
   *Chorus*

CHORUS
My dear! My dear! My dear!
Oh my dear dark-eyed *Magdeline*,
You la la la la la la! You la la la la la la!
No peace you leave me, dear!

*A German word meaning "my little maiden."

# Liebes Mädchen, hör' mir zu

### (LOVELY MAIDEN, HEAR ME, LO)

Translation by Hedi Salzer
Versification by Freda Morrill Abrams

Joseph Haydn

*Allegretto*

Lie - bes Mäd - chen, hör' mir zu, öff - ne leis' das Git - ter;
Love - ly maid - en, soft - ly, lo, From your win - dow hear me,

denn mein Herz hat kei - ne Ruh', kei - ne Ruh' die Zi - ther.
For no peace does my heart know, Song will bring you near me.

Hal - ten Klos - ter - mau - ern dich noch so streng ge - bun - den,
Though the clois - ter walls so strong Still so firm - ly hold you,

ha - ben mei - ne Lie - der sich    doch zu dir ge - fun - den.
Yet my zith - er's yearn - ing song    Ris - es to en - fold    you.

2. When the dusky shadows fall,
   Evening mists hang over,
   Then I climb up to your wall,
   Branches aid your lover.
   If, my fair imprisoned one,
   You'll but bow down toward me,
   'Spite of abbess, priest or nun,
   You will well reward me.

# O, cessate di piagarmi
### (O, I PRAY YOU, DO NOT WOUND ME)

English version by Freda Morrill Abrams

Alessandro Scarlatti

di - spie - ta - te, più del ge - lo e, più di mar - mi,
pit - i - less, hate - ful. She is i - cy, she's like mar - ble,

fred - de e sor - de a miei mar - tir,
Deaf and cold to such as I,

fred - de e sor - de a miei mar - tir.
Deaf and cold to such as I.

O, ces - sa - te di pia - gar - mi, o, la - scia - te -
O, I pray you, do not wound me. Leave me, leave me,

mi mo - rir,
let me die,

o, la - scia - te - mi mo - rir!
Leave me, leave me, let me die!

# CELESTE AÏDA

### (FAIREST AÏDA)

### From "Aïda"

English version by Freda Morrill Abrams

Giuseppe Verdi

*Andantino*
*con espressione*

Ce - le - ste A-ï - da, ___ for - ma di - vi - na, ___

Fair - est ___ A - ï - da, ___ Heav - en - ly glo - ry, ___

mi - sti - co ser - to di lu - ce e fior;
Mys - ti - cal vi - sion Of flow'rs and light.

del mio pen - sie - ro tu sei re - gi - na, tu di mia
Queen of my soul, You reign su - preme - ly, You of my

vi - ta sei lo splen - dor.
life are the splen - dor bright.

Il tuo bel cie - lo vor - rei ri - dar - ti, le dol - ci
To your fair sky, O I would re - store you, To gen - tle

*vi - na, _____ mi - sti - co*
glo - ry, _____ Mys - ti - cal

*rag - gio di lu - ce e*
vi - sion of flow'rs ___ and

*fior; del mio _____ pen -*
light; Queen of _____ my

ser - to sul crin po- sar- ti, er ger-ti un tro- no vi - ci - no al
gar - land I would crown o'er you, And near the sun, I would raise your

sol, un tro- no vi - ci - no al sol, un tro- no vi - ci - no al
throne, Your throne, I would raise your throne, Your throne, I would raise your

sol.
throne.

# My Love Is Gone to Sea

Francis Hopkinson

*Simply—not too fast*

1. My_ love is gone to sea Whilst I his ab - sence mourn,_ No_
2. One_ lit - tle month was past, And_ who so blest as we,_ The_

joy shall smile on me_____ Un - til my love_ re - turn.__ He_
sum - mons came at last_____ And Jem - my must_ to_ sea,__ I_

ask'd me for his bride, And_ man - y vows he_ swore,_ I_
saw his ship so gay Swift fly the wave-worn_ shore,_ I_

blushed and soon com - plied,___ I __ blushed and soon com -
wiped my tears a - way,_____ I __ wiped my tears a -

plied,_____ My heart was his__ be - fore,___ My heart was
way,_____ And saw his ship_ no__ more, ___ No more, no

*slower*

his, My heart was his__ be - fore._____
more, And saw his ship_ no__ more._____

*slower*

3. When clouds shut in the sky,
   And storms around me howl,
   When livid light'nings fly
   And threatening thunders roll,
   All hopes of rest are lost,
   No slumbers visit me,
   My anxious thoughts are toss'd,
   My anxious thoughts are toss'd
   With Jemmy on the sea,
   My thoughts are toss'd
   With Jemmy on the sea.

# How Should I Your True Love Know?

William Shakespeare

From *Hamlet, Prince of Denmark*

*Slowly and simply*

1. How should I your true love know From an-oth-er one?
2. He is dead and gone, la - dy, He is dead and gone:

By his cock-le hat and staff And his san-dal shoon.
At his head a grass green turf, At his heels a stone.

# Im wunderschönen Monat Mai

## (IN WONDROUS LOVELY MAY)

Heinrich Heine
Translation by Hedi Salzer
Versification by Freda Morrill Abrams

Robert Schumann

*With free flowing motion*

Im wun - der-schö-nen Mo-nat Mai,     als
In May,   in won-drous love-ly May,     As

al - le Knos-pen spran-gen,     da ist   in mei - nem
all   the buds __ were flow - 'ring,   I felt   from deep with-

Her - zen die Lie - be auf - ge - gan - gen.
in me Love's yearn - ing ov - er - pow'r -ing.

rit.

a tempo *p*

Im
In

a tempo

wun - der - schö - nen Mo - nat Mai, als
May, in won - drous love - ly May, As

al - le Vö - gel san - gen, da hab' ich ihr ge-
all the birds___ were sing - ing, Then have I come be-

stan - den mein Seh - nen und Ver - lan - gen.
fore her, My love and ar - dor bring - ing.

rit. - - - - - - - -

# Have You Seen But a White Lily Grow?

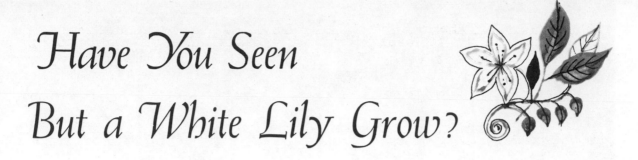

Ben Jonson

Have you seen but a white li-ly grow _____ Be-

fore rude hands have touch'd it? Have you mark'd but _ the _ fall of the

snow Be - fore _ the earth hath smutch'd it? Have you felt the wool of

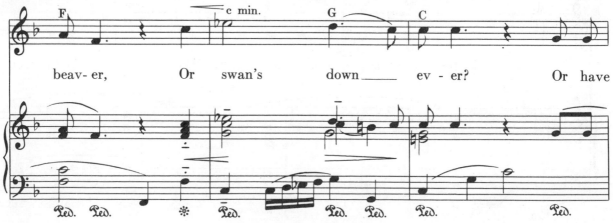

beav- er,        Or     swan's        down____ ev - er?        Or have

smelt of the bud of the briar, Or the nard in the fire? Or have

# Then You'll Remember Me

From *"The Bohemian Girl"*

Alfred Dunn

Michael William Balfe

1. When oth - er lips and oth - er hearts their
   cold - ness or de - ceit shall slight the

tales of love shall tell
beau - ty now they prize,

In lan - guage whose ex -
And deem it but a

cess im - parts the pow'r they feel so well;
fa - ded light which beams with - in your eyes;

There
When

may per - haps in such a \_\_ scene some re - col - lec - tion
hol - low \_ hearts shall wear \_ a \_ mask, 'twill break your own \_ to

be Of days that have as hap - py \_ been, and
see; In such a mo - ment I \_ but \_ ask that

you'll re - mem - ber me, _____ And you'll re - mem-ber, you'll re-mem - ber
you'll re - mem - ber me, _____ That you'll re - mem-ber, you'll re-mem - ber

me.
me.

*a tempo*

*a tempo*

1.

2.

2. When

# COME AGAIN

John Dowland

*Freely, with motion*

1. Come a-gain, sweete love doth now in-vite Thy
2. Come a-gain, that I may cease to mourne Through

grac-es that re-fraine, To do me due de-light.
thy un-kind dis-daine, For now, left and for-lorne,

To see, to heare, to touch, to kisse, to die \
I sit, I sigh, I weep, I faint, I die \
With thee a-gaine in sweet-est sym-pa-thy. \
In dead-ly paine and end-less mis-er-y.

3. Gentle love draw forth thy wounding dart;
   Thou canst not pierce her heart,
   For I that do approve
   By sighs and teares more hot than are thy shafts
   Did tempt, while she for triumph laughs.

# VEDRAI, CARINO

(DARLING, I'LL SHOW YOU)

From "*Don Giovanni*"

English version by Freda Morrill Abrams

Wolfgang Amadeus Mozart

*Ve - drai, ca - ri - no, Se sei buo - ni - no,*
Dar - ling, I'll show _ you, Some-thing you know too,

*Che bel ri - me - dio Ti vog - lio dar. _*
A fine old rem-e - dy,'Twill cure you, dear. _

È na-tu-ra-le,      Non dà dis-gu-sto,
Of na-ture's giv-ing,      Not hard to take it,

È lo spe-cia-le, Non lo sa l'ar, no,    Non lo sa l'ar, no,
The joy of liv-ing, Noth-ing to fear, no,    Noth-ing to fear, no,

*poco rit.*      *a tempo*

Non lo sa l'ar,_____ È un cer-to bal-sa-mo Che por-to
Noth-ing to fear._____ A bal-sam sooth-ing I car-ry

ad - dos - so, Da - re te'l pos - so, Se il vuoi pro - var. ___
with ___ me. Say, will you give ___ me One try right here? ___

Sa - per vor - res - ti?
Oh, can you guess it?

Do - ve mi sta, Do - ve, do - ve, Do - ve, mi sta? _____
Stand by me near, Stand by, stand by, Stand by me near! _____

Sen - ti - lo bat - te - re,
Just feel it beat - ing now,

Sen - ti - lo ___ bat - te - re, ___ Toc - ca mi qua! ___ qua! ___ qua! ___
Just feel it ___ beat-ing now, ___ Touch my heart here! ___ here! ___ here! ___

Sen - ti - lo bat - te - re, Toc - ca mi qua, qua! Toc - ca mi qua, qua!
Just _ feel _ it _ beat-ing _ now, Touch my heart here, here! Touch my heart here, here!

Toc - ca mi qua! _ qua! Toc - ca mi qua!
Touch my heart here, _ here! Touch my heart here!

# Lehn' deine Wang' an meine Wang'

(O PRESS YOUR CHEEK UPON MY OWN)

Heinrich Heine
Translation by Hedi Salzer
Versification by Freda Morrill Abrams

Adolf Jensen

*Lehn' dei - ne Wang'*
O press your cheek

*an mei - ne Wang', dann flie - ssen die Thrä - nen zu - sam - men,*
up-on my own, Our tears will to - geth - er be flow - ing,

*und an mein Herz, drück' fest dein Herz, dann schla - gen zu - sam - men die*
And press your heart close to my heart, To - geth - er we're flam - ing and

Flam - men. Und wenn in die gro - sse Flam - me fliesst der
glow - ing. And when through our flow - ing tears at last Love's

Strom von un - sern Thrä - nen, und wenn mein Arm dich ge -
flame is bright - ly burn - ing, And when my arms shall en -

wal - tig um - schliesst, sterb' ich vor Lie - bes - seh - nen.
cir - cle you fast, Then I shall die of yearn - ing.

Lehn' dei - ne Wang' an mei - ne Wang'!
O press your cheek up - on my own.

# Was ist Sylvia?

(WHO IS SYLVIA?)

William Shakespeare
From *Two Gentlemen of Verona*
Translated into German by E. von Bauernfeld

Franz Schubert

Was        ist    Syl - via,
Who        is     Syl - via,

246

# AMARILLI

Giovanni Battista Guarini

English version by Lyndal Brandeis

Giulio Caccini

*Freely - with passion*

A - ma - ril - li, mia bel - la, non cre - dio, del mio

A - ma - ril - li, my fair - est, Say, can you not be -

cor dol - ce de - si - o, d'es - ser tu
lieve, Heart's sweet de - sired one, That you are

_ l'a - mor mi - o? Cre - di - lo pur, e se ti
_ my be - lov - ed? Do but be - lieve, And if a

mor t'as - sa - le, du - bi - tar non ti va - le.
fear tor - ment you Let this proof then con - tent you.

250

A - prim' il pet - to e ve - drai scrit-to in co - re: A - ma -
Look in my heart, __ And see these words in - scrib - ed: A - ma -

ril - li, A - ma - ril - li, A - ma -
ril - li, A - ma - ril - li, A - ma -

ril - li è'l mio a - mo - re; A - ma - ril -
ril - li, be - lov - ed. A - ma - ril -

li è'l mio a - mo - re.
li, be - lov - ed.

# GRUSS

## (GREETING)

Heinrich Heine
Translation by Hedi Salzer
Versification by Freda Morrill Abrams

Felix Mendelssohn

Lei - se zieht durch mein Ge - müth lieb - li - ches Ge - läu - te;
Gen - tly in my thoughts I hear Sweet - est bells a - sing - ing.

254

klin - ge, klei - nes Früh - lings - lied, kling' hin - aus ins
Sing out, lit - tle Spring song dear, Far and wide be

Wei - - - te.
ring - - - ing.

2. To the house where violets grow
   Quickly go a-winging.
   Should you spy a lovely rose,
   Greet her for me, singing!

# OH, MY LOVE

## (A ROUND)

English song

Oh, my love, lov'st thou me? Then quick-ly come and save him that dies for thee. Oh, my love, lov'st thou me? Then quick-ly come and save him that dies for thee.

# Go to Joan Glover

(A ROUND)

English song

*Allegro moderato*

(1) Go to Joan Glov - er and

(2) Tell her I love her and

(3) By the light of the moon

(4) I will come to her.

# Joan, Come Kiss Me Now

(A ROUND)

English song

(1) g min.    F    g min.    D

Joan,   come kiss   me   now.

(2) g min.    F    g min.    D

Once a-gain   for my love,   gen - tle

(3) g min.    F    g min.    D

Joan,   Come kiss   me   now.

# Beautiful Dreamer

Words and music by Stephen Foster

*Moderato*

1. Beau-ti-ful dream-er, wake un-to me, _____
2. Beau-ti-ful dream-er, out on the sea _____

Star-light and dew-drops are wait-ing for thee; _____
Mer-maids are chant-ing the wild lo-re-lie; _____

# L'AMOUR DE MOI

## (MY LOVE IN GARDEN SPOT IS DWELLING)

English version by Freda Morrill Abrams

French song

With a flow

*L'a- mour de moi  sy est en- clo- - - se*
1. My  love in gar- den spot is  dwell- - - -
2. Oh  lis- ten now,  is aught more  thrill- - -

*De  dans un  jo- lie___ jar- di- net.*
Gar- den fair  where soft___ breez- es  blow,
Than  the night- in - gale's___ dul- cet  lay?

*Où  crôit la  rose ___ et le ___  mu- guet  Et aus- si*
There blooms the  rose ___ and lil- ies  grow,  And hol- ly ___
All  eve- ning long ___ till break ___ of  day  He sings  till

fait le pas - se - ro - - - se.
hocks of sum - mer tell - - - ing.
he must rest from trill - - - ing.

Ce jar - din est bel et ____ plai - sant. Il est gar -
This gar - den is so ve - ry fair With flow - ers
I saw her cull - ing on ____ the lea Vi - o - lets

ni de tou - tes fleurs. On y prend son é -
fra - grant, col - or gay, One finds much joy to
from the mead - ow green. Sweet is the flow'r, but

bat - te - ment Au - tant la nuit ____ comme ____ le jour.
vis - it there, Wheth - er by night ____ or ____ by day.
sweet - er she, Love - li - est maid ____ ev - er seen.

*poco rit.* D.C.

264

3. I watched her there in gar-den go- - -ing, She was fresh, so milk-y white and fair, To gen-tle lamb she did com-pare, Like blush - ing rose her beau-ty glow- - ing.

# Nur, wer die Sehnsucht kennt

(NONE BUT A LOVER KNOWS)

Johann Wolfgang von Goethe

English version by Freda Morrill Abrams

Peter Ilich Tchaikovsky

With pedal

von al - ler Freu - de!  Es schwin - delt
No more re - turn - ing,  My heart - sick

mir, _____ es brennt mein Ein - ge - wei - de.
long - - - ing grows, My in - ner burn - ing.

Nur, wer die Sehn-sucht kennt, weiss, was  ich  lei - de!
None but a lov - er knows My  lone - ly  yearn - ing.

# Du bist die Ruh'

## (THOU ART REPOSE)

Heinrich Heine
Translation by Hedi Salzer
Versification by Freda Morrill Abrams

Franz Schubert

Du bist die Ruh', der Frie - de mild,
Thou art re - pose, tran - quil - i - ty,

die Sehn - sucht du, und was sie stillt;
My long - ing knows its rest in thee.

Ich wei - he dir _____ voll Lust und Schmerz, zur Woh - nung
I of - fer thee _____ love's joy and pain. Light of my

*poco rit.*

hier _____ mein Aug' und Herz, _____ mein Aug' und Herz. _____
soul, _____ with me re - main, _____ with me re - main. _____

*a tempo*

Kehr' ein bei mir, und schlie - sse du *still hin - ter*
Come back to me, and gen - tly close So si - lent -

*dir die Pfor - ten zu. Trieb' an - dern Schmerz*
ly the wait - ing doors. Drive oth - er cares

*aus_die - ser_ Brust, voll sei dies Herz,_ von_ dei - ner_*
from out_my_ breast. Let heart be full,_ by_ thee_ be_

Dies Au - gen - zelt, von dei - nem Glanz al -
This splen - dor bright, it comes from thee. This

lein er - hellt, ___ o - füll, es ___ ganz, ___
heav'n - ly light, ___ O ___ fill ___ thou ___ me, ___

o ___ füll, es ___ ganz! ___
O ___ fill ___ thou ___ me! ___

# I Prethee,
# Send Me Back My Heart

Dr. Henry Hughes

Henry Lawes

Gently
mp

1. I pre - thee, send me back my heart, Since
2. Yet now I think on't, let it lie, To

rit. - - - - - - a tempo

I can - not have thine; For if from yours you
send it me were vain, For th'hast a thief in

will not part, Why then should you keep mine?
ei - ther eye Will steal it back a - gain!

3. Then farewell care and farewell woe,
   I will no longer pine,
   But I'll believe I have her heart
   As much as she has mine.

# Once I Loved a Maiden Fair

English song

*Not too fast*

**mf**  G   b min.   a min. b min. e min.   a min.   D7   G

1. Once I loved a maid-en fair, But she did de - ceive me;
2. Three times I did make it known To the con - gre - ga - tion

*mf*

G   b min.   a min.   b min. e min.   a min.   D7   G

She with Ve - nus might com - pare ___ In my mind, be - lieve me.
That the Church should make us one As priest had made re - la - tion.

She was young and a - mong __ Crea - tures of temp - ta - tion;
Mar - ried we straight must be, Al - though we go a - beg - ging;

*Just a bit slower*

Who will say but maid - ens may __ Kiss for re - cre - a - tion?
Now, a - las! 'tis like to prove A ve - ry hope - less wed - ding.

*Just a bit slower*

# O ma tendre musette

## (PIPES, OH SO SWEETLY RINGING)

Jean François de Laharpe

English versification by Freda Morrill Abrams

Pierre A. Monsigny

Andante

O ma ten-dre mu-set - te, mu-set-te des a - mours,___
Pipes, oh so sweet-ly ring - ing, Chant-ing a lov - er's praise,___

toi qui chan-tais Li-set - te, Li - sette et les beaux jours.___
You of Li-sette were sing - ing, Li - sette and hap -py days.___

*D'u- ne vaine es - pé - ran - ce    Tu m'a-vais trop flat - té.* ___
With vain hope you  de - ceived    me    That she would ans - wer "yes." ___

*Chan - te son in - cons-tan - ce    et ma fi - dé - li - té.* ___
Sing  now of how she grieves  me    And of  my faith- ful- ness. ___

2. Surely love's burning fire
   Shone in her eyes so bright.
   I thought the same desire
   Filled her soul with delight.
   Lisette, at her beginning
   Embodied pleasure gay,
   Oh, she's so young and winning,
   Can she know to betray?

3. Pipes, oh so sweetly playing,
   Comfort me in despair.
   My Lisette's name be saying,
   For joy her name doth bear.
   I see her beauty growing
   More lovely than before,
   I will lament her knowing
   I'll love her ever more!

# Wir wandelten

## (WE WANDERED)

Translation by Hedi Salzer

Versification by Freda Morrill Abrams

Johannes Brahms

Wir wan - del - ten, wir

We wan - dered, we

zwei zu - sam - men,      ich ___ war so still und
two to - geth - er.      I ___ was so still, and

du so stil - le;    ich gä - be viel,    um zu er -
you so si - lent;    Much would I give    could I dis -

fah - ren, was du ge - dacht in je - nem Fall.    Was
cov - er What you were think-ing on that day.    What

ich ge - dacht, un - aus - ge - spro - chen ver - blei - be
I was think-ing on that day ___ Will un - spo - ken

das!     Nur Ei -   nes sag' ich,     Ei -   nes sag' ___
be!     But this   I tell you,     this   I tell ___

ich:     So   schön war Al -   les, was _ ich _ dach - te,
you:     All   of   my   thoughts then were _ so _ love - ly;

so himm - lisch hei - ter war __ es __ all'!
Such heav'n - ly joy they did __ con - vey!

In mei - nem Haup - te die __ Ge - dan - ken,
For in my mind the thoughts were __ sing - ing

sie läu - te - ten wie gold' - ne __ Glöck - chen;
Like gold - en bells so sweet - ly __ ring - ing.

so wun - der-süss, so wun - der - lieb -
So won - drous sweet, so won - drous love -

# Voi, che sapete

(YOU WHO ARE KNOWING)

From *"The Marriage of Figaro"*

English version by Freda Morrill Abrams

Wolfgang Amadeus Mozart

*mp*

Voi,    che sa - pe - te    che   co - s'è a - mor,
You,    who are know - ing    Love's   se - cret __ lore,

Don - ne ve - de - te,    s'io   l'ho nel cor,
Pray,   is Love show - ing    At    my heart's core?

Don - ne, ve - de - te,__ s'io   l'ho _ nel _ cor.
Pray,__ is Love show - ing __ At    my_heart's core?

Quel - lo ch'io pro - vo, vi \_\_\_ ri - di - rò, \_\_\_
This that I'm feel - ing, I \_\_\_ will speak true, \_

È per me nuo - vo ca - pir no'l so.
Is, I'm ap - peal - ing, For \_\_\_ me, quite new!

Sen - to un af - fet - to pien di de - sir, \_\_\_
I feel af - fec - tion, full of de - sire, \_

Ch'o - ra è di - let - to, ch'o - ra è mar - tir.
Now it's per - fec - tion, Now tor - ment dire!

Ge - lo, e poi sen - to l'al - ma av - vam - par,
Now I am freez - ing, Then I will burn,

E in un mo - men - to tor - no a ge - lar.
Ar - dor then seiz - ing, To ice I turn!

Ri - cer-co un be - ne fuo - ri di me,
Treas - ure I'm seek - ing Be - yond me now.

Non so ch'il tie - ne, non so cos' è. So - spi-ro e
What am I seek - ing, How find it, how? Not of my

ge - mo sen-za vo - ler, Pal - pi-to e tre - mo sen-za sa -
mak - ing, I groan and sigh, Trem - bling and shak - ing, I don't know

291

per.   *Non tro-vo pa-ce not-te, nè di, ma pur mi*
why.   I find no lei-sure By night or day, Yet I find

*pia - ce lan - guir co - sì.*   *Voi, che sa-*
pleas - ure suff - 'ring this way!   You, who are

*pe - te che, co - s è a - mor,*   *Don - ne, ve -*
know - ing Love's se - cret lore,   Pray, is Love

*de - te, s'io l'ho nel cor,*   *Don - ne, ve -*
show - ing At my heart's core?   Pray,___ is Love

de - te,___ s'io l'ho nel cor,  Don - ne, ve -
show - ing___ At my heart's core?  Pray,___ is Love

de - te,___ s'io l'ho_nel_cor.
show - ing___ At my_heart's core?

# Where'er You Walk

From the oratorio *"Semele"*

Alexander Pope

George Frederick Handel

Where - 'er you_walk, cool gales shall fan the glade; Trees, where you_ sit, shall crowd in - to a shade, Trees where you_ sit, shall crowd in -

to ___ a shade;

Where - 'er you walk, cool gales shall fan the _ glade;

Trees, where you sit, shall crowd in - to a _ shade, ____

Trees, where you sit, shall crowd__ in-

to __ a shade.

Where - 'er you__ tread, the blush-ing flow'rs shall rise, And

297

all things flour-ish and all things flour-ish Where -

'er you turn your eyes, where-'er you turn your eyes, where-'er you turn your eyes.

# O wie lieblich ist das Mädchen

(O HOW LOVELY IS THE MAIDEN)

Emanuel Geibel

English translation by Hedi Salzer

Robert Schumann

*Not too fast*

O wie lie - blich ist das Mäd-chen,
O how love-ly is the maid-en,

wie so schön und voll An - mut, ___ wie so schön!
O how fair and so grace - ful, ___ O how fair!

Sag' mir an, du wack-rer See-man,
Tell me, pray, you heart-y sail-or,

der du lebst auf dei - nem Schif-fe, ob das
You who live up - on your ves-sel, If your

Schiff und sei - ne Se - gel, ob die Ster - ne wohl so schön, so
ship and all her rig - ging, If the stars so clear a - bove Are

schön _____ sind?
like _____ her!

2. Oh how lovely is the maiden,
   O how fair and so graceful,
   O how fair!
   Tell me, pray, you knight so gallant,
   You who walk in shining armor,
   If your horse and if your armor,
   If the spirit of the fight
   Are like her!

3. O how lovely is the maiden,
   O how fair and so graceful,
   O how fair!
   Tell me, pray, you friendly shepherd,
   You who lead your flocks to pasture
   If your flocks and if your pasture,
   If the mountains high above
   Are like her!

4. O how love-ly is the maid-en, O how fair and so

grace-ful, _____ O how fair and so grace - ful, _____ O how

fair!

# Frag', ob die Rose

(ASK IF YON DAMASK ROSE BE SWEET)

From "Susanna"

George Frederick Handel

Moderato

Frag', ob die Ro - se süss_ von Duft, die rings-um_ würzt die_
Ask if yon dam-ask rose_ be sweet, That scents the_ am - bient

Luft; dann frag' die Schä - fer auf_ den Höh'n, ob nicht mein_Mäd-chen_
air; Then ask each shep-herd that_ you meet, If dear Su - san - na's_

schön, ob nicht, ob nicht mein Mäd-chen schön,ob nicht mein Mäd-chen_
fair. If dear,_ dear Su - san - na's fair, If dear Su - san - na's_

rit.

schön? Frag', ob die Ro - se süss _ von _ Duft, die rings -um _ würzt die _
fair. Ask if yon dam - ask rose _ be _ sweet, That scents the _ am - bient

Luft;    *dann frag' die Schä - fer*   *auf den Höh'n, ob*   *nicht mein Mäd-chen*
air;    Then ask each shep - herd that you meet If dear Su - san-na's

schön,    *ob*   *nicht mein Mäd - chen schön?*
fair,    If dear Su - san - na's fair.

2. Say, will the vulture leave his prey,
   And warble thro' the grove?
   Bid wanton linnets quit the spray,
   Then doubt thy shepherd's love,
   Then doubt thy shepherd's love,
   Then doubt thy shepherd's love.
   Say, will the vulture leave his prey
   And warble thro' the grove?
   Bid wanton linnets quit the spray,
   Then doubt thy shepherd's love,
   Then doubt thy shepherd's love.

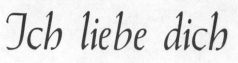

# Ich liebe dich

## (I LOVE YOU)

German translation by F. von Holstein
(From the original Danish by Hans Christian Andersen)
English version by Freda Morrill Abrams

Edvard Grieg

Du mein Ge-
You are my

dan-ke, du mein Sein und Wer- den, du mei-nes
thoughts, my end and my be-gin- ning, Joy of my

Her-zens er- ste Se-lig-keit!
heart, the one that I a-dore,

Ich lie - be dich wie nichts auf die - ser Er - den, ich
More than all else on earth or un - der heav - en I

mf
cresc.

lie - be dich,    ich lie - be dich,    ich lie - be dich in Zeit und
love you, dear,    I love you, dear,    I love you now and will for -

f broadly

E - wig-keit!    Ich lie - be dich in Zeit und E - wig-keit!
ev - er-more!    I love you now and will for - ev - er-more!

a tempo

1.    2.

2. On - ly to

p

2. Only to you my thoughts must be returning,
Devoted to your joy my heart shall be;
Whatever fate God has for my life's turning,
I love you, dear, I love you, dear,
I love you now and for eternity!
I love you now and for eternity!

# VOLKSLIEDCHEN

(AS I WALK IN THE GARDEN DEW)

Translation by Hedi Salzer
Versification by Freda Morrill Abrams

Robert Schumann

*Wenn ich früh in den Gar - ten geh', in mei - nem grü - nen Hut,*
As I walk in the gar - den dew I wear my green hat gay,

*ist mein er - ster Ge - dan - ke, was nun mein Lieb - ster*
First of all I am wond'ring, How fares my love to -

*thut?*
day?

Am
I'd

Him - mel steht kein Stern, den ich dem Freund nicht gönn - te, mein
give you from the sky The bright - est star a - bove you! My

Herz gäb' ich ihm gern, wenn ich's her - aus thun könn - te!
heart I'd give, but I Am sure you know it loves you!

Wenn ich früh in den Gar - ten geh', in mei - nem grü - nen Hut, ist mein
As I walk in the gar - den dew I wear my green hat gay, First of

er - ster Ge - dan - ke, was nun mein Lieb - ster thut, ist mein
all I am wond'ring, How fares my love to - day? First of

# PASSING BY

Words from Thomas Ford's *Music of Sundry Kinds*

Edward Purcell

1. There is a la-dy sweet and kind, Was nev-er
   face so pleas'd my mind; I did but see her
   pass-ing by, And yet I love her till I die.

2. Her ges-tures, mo-tions and her smiles, Her wit, her
   voice my heart be-guiles, Be-guiles my heart, I
   know not why, And yet I love her till I die.

3. Cu-pid is wing-ed and doth range, Doth range her
   coun-try, so my love doth change; But change the earth, or
   change the sky, Yet will I love her till I die.

# Jungfräulein, soll ich mit euch geh'n?

(DEAR MAIDEN, SHALL I WITH YOU GO?)

Translation by Hedi Salzer
Versification by Freda Morrill Abrams

Johannes Brahms

*Fast, delicately*

"Jung-fräu-lein, soll ich mit euch geh'n in eu'-ren Ro-sen-gar-ten, da

1. "Dear maid-en, shall I with you go In - to your gar - den fair, ___ There

3. "But in my dar - ling's gar - den So man-y flow-ers grow, ___ Would

to my gar-den you can't go So ear-ly in the day. The
friend, a-bout that which you say, It can and may not be, You'd

*p* lightly

gar-den's key you can-not find, It's hid-den fast a-way. It
sure-ly tram-ple down one day My dear-est flow'rs for me. So

lies so well pro-tect-ed, So guard-ed is this key, That
turn a-way from here now, Go home, I beg of you, You'd

he must learn love's wis - dom, Who ope's the gate for
bring me to dis - hon - or, In truth, that would not

me."
do."

*pp* with more sentiment

5. There high up - on that moun - tain The mill wheel turns no

more, It grinds not night nor day - time, Like love, its work is

o'er. The mill wheel has been brok - en, And love is at an

*pp gradually dying away*

end, So "God bless you, my sweet - heart, Now Mis - 'ry's way I

wend."

# INDEX OF FIRST LINES

319

# INDEX OF TITLES

# ABOUT THE CONTRIBUTORS

## THE EDITOR

MARGARET BRADFORD BONI says of herself: "I was born in Birmingham, Alabama, and lived in Tallahassee, Florida, from the age of one until I finished college—Florida State College. Studied music in Germany for a year, then studied at the Institute of Musical Art (now the Juilliard School of Music). Decided to go into school music and worked with Hollis Dann, state supervisor of music in Pennsylvania, for my supervisor's degree.

"I taught music in the public schools in Factoryville, Pennsylvania, at the Brearley School in New York City, and at the City and Country School, where I am now.

"Besides editing the *Fireside Book of Folk Songs* and *Fireside Book of Favorite American Songs*, I have written six books of material for the recorder and published a collection of songs for very young children, *Keep Singing, Keep Humming*. I have also given recorder courses in the Department of General Education, New York University."

## THE ARRANGER

NORMAN LLOYD, a member of the faculty of the Juilliard School of Music, was born in Pottsville, Pennsylvania. He has received the B.S. and M.A. degrees in Music Education from New York University, studied piano with Abbey Whiteside and William O'Toole, and explored composition with Vincent Jones and Aaron Copland. As music director of the Bennington School of Dance and of the Humphrey-Weidman Dance Company, and conductor of the Sarah Lawrence College Chorus, he became a seasoned conductor. He has taught music at New York University, Sarah Lawrence College, the Humphrey-Weidman Dance Studio, the Hanya Holm School of Dance, and, finally, at the Juilliard School. Among his recent compositions are the words and music for a choral ballet, *Restless Land*, music for documentary films, and several ballets for José Limón. Mr. Lloyd was the arranger also of both the *Fireside Book of Folk Songs* and the *Fireside Book of Favorite American Songs*.

## THE ARTISTS

The biographies of ALICE and MARTIN PROVENSEN are practically the same. Both were born in Chicago, both won scholarships at and attended the Chicago Art Institute, both attended the University of California, and both worked in Hollywood in the production of animated-cartoon films— Alice for Universal, and Martin for the Disney Studio. They did not meet, however, until Martin had joined the Navy and was assigned to Navy training film work at the studio where Alice was working. They then immediately decided to join forces and collaborate in earnest for the rest of their lives. They are now established book illustrators; three of their books have been named among the "Fifty Books of the Year" by the American Institute of Graphic Arts: *Fireside Book of Folk Songs, The Golden Mother Goose,* and *A Child's Garden of Verses*. Other titles they have illustrated include *The Fireside Cook Book* and *The Golden Bible: The New Testament*.

\*

The music in this book was hand-drawn throughout
by MAXWELL WEANER.